The Masters COLLECTION

The Godowsky
COLLECTION, Vol. 1
ORIGINAL COMPOSITIONS
FOR PIANO SOLO

The Publisher wishes to thank Mr. Leopold Godowsky III for his assistance, support, and generosity in supplying materials used to help create this volume.

Compilation and Introductory Notes
by Dr Millan Sachania

CARL FISCHER®
65 Bleecker Street, New York, NY 10012

ATF122

ISBN 0-8258-1130-9

Table of Contents
Vol. 1: Original Compositions for Piano Solo

Leopold Godowsky : Volume 1

Introductory Essay by Dr Millan Sachania

In 1928 Ernest Newman, the British music critic, remarked that 'Godowsky is not really interested in other men's music unless he wrote it himself'.[1] In the same year, Sir Donald Tovey coined the phrase 'to Godowskify the classics'.[2] Each had in mind Godowsky the arranger. For then, as now, the arrangements virtually eclipsed Godowsky's corpus of original compositions; as Paul Bekker commented, Godowsky's name had come to suggest only "arrangements" and "adaptations" for the pianist with technical equipment'.[3] True enough, the early free compositions, issued from 1888 (when Godowsky was eighteen), had given way to a spate of radical, audacious arrangements: fifty-three 'studies' on Chopin's études (1894–1914), two other Chopin paraphrases (1899), some Weber arrangements (1903–05), a collection of Baroque arrangements entitled *Renaissance* (1906 and 1909), and 'symphonic metamorphoses' on waltzes by Johann Strauss II (1912). The evidence suggests that Godowsky wanted his compositional skills to mature in these years,[4] and one might wonder to what extent Godowsky conceived of the arranging process as a means of compositional improvement. (The only formal 'lessons' he had had were during his twelve unhappy weeks at the Berlin Hochschule für Musik in 1883, where his composition teachers included Clara Schumann's half-brother Woldemar Bargiel.) If indeed arranging served—even if only in part—as a form of self-instruction, then 1911 marked the end of Godowsky's compositional 'apprenticeship' with the publication of the Sonata (which was begun in 1896). This monumental *opus* was followed by sets such as *Walzermasken* (1912), *Triakontameron* (1919), and, for piano duet, *Miniatures* (1918). Meanwhile, the production of arrangements slowed considerably until Godowsky's interest revived in the 1920s. Generally more conservative than the earlier batch, these later arrangements include 'elaborations' of three of Bach's solo violin sonatas and partitas, and three of the solo cello suites (1924), five concert versions of Chopin's waltzes (1921–27), and two Albéniz reworkings (1921 and 1928). The flow of free compositions from Godowsky's atelier continued, however, and the 1920s saw the publication of the 'Java' Suite (1925), the Passacaglia on Schubert's 'Unfinished' (1928), some 'Waltz Poems' (1929–30), and a selection of works for the left hand alone, a medium which Godowsky had first explored in his 'studies' on Chopin's études.

Godowsky's reputation as a composer never wholly recovered from the critical 'Niagaras of abuse'—as K. S. Sorabji memorably put it[5]—which buffeted his 'studies' on Chopin's études. 'Godowsky the arranger' being understood as an extension of 'Godowsky the pianist', not of 'Godowsky the composer', such arrangements were generally judged as sinful aberrations in the service of Godowsky's recitals rather than as potentially valuable entities in their own right. The broad critical consensus was that the arrangements aimed at 'improving' the classics, 'modernizing' them, or amplifying their technical difficulties. Accordingly, Godowsky was indicted with 'damaging' the works he treated, with threatening the originals' standing in the repertory, with irreverence, and with compositional deficiency.[6] It was as if Godowsky were compensating for his lack of inspiration by feeding parasitically on other composers' blood. Indeed, the conservatism of the later arrangements might well have been due, in part, to Godowsky's desire to escape such strictures: he complained that he could not face any more charges of 'sacrilege, self-advertising, conceit, lack of ideas of my own, and what not'.[7] Not that critical opinion was much more positive about the free compositions. 'Will Godowsky the composer for piano share honors with the instrumentalist?' pondered a critic in *Musical America* in 1928.[8] The *Musical Times* thought not, at least not in the perception of the general public.[9] The journal held Godowsky culpable for failing 'to follow the example of the classics [by not writing] a few fairly easy and attractive things for the domestic performer', adding that 'it was a fatal omission on the part of Godowsky and Busoni to give us no Consolation in E, no Minuet in G, no Prelude in C sharp minor'. But Godowsky in fact produced much that could be tackled successfully by the amateur pianist; indeed, 'Alt Wien', from *Triakontameron*, became a minor classic. The free compositions surely suffered because they unwittingly became the victims of the critical ammunition fired at the arrangements. Even 'Alt Wien' eventually succumbed to the onslaught.

Much of the critical censure was, needless to say, ill founded and prejudiced. Carl Engel's comments of 1923

[1] 'Arrangements—by Godowsky and Others', *Sunday Times* (London), 22 April 1928, p. 7.

[2] 'Tonality in Schubert', in *Essays in Musical Analysis : Chamber Music* (London, 1944), p. 145.

[3] 'A Note', in Leopold Godowsky, *Operatic Masterpieces* (New York, 1936).

[4] See my comments on the origins of the E minor Sonata later in this essay.

[5] 'Leopold Godowsky as Creative Transcriber', in *Mi Contra Fa : The Immoralisings of a Machiavellian Musician* (London, 1947), pp. 62–70 (p. 68).

[6] For a discussion of these issues, see my '"Improving the Classics" : Some Thoughts on the "Ethics" and Aesthetics of Musical Arrangement', *Music Review* 55 (1994), pp. 58–75.

[7] Godowsky quoted in Clarence Lucas, 'A Chat with Godowsky', *Musical Courier* (New York), 9 August 1928, p. 14.

[8] Sydney Dalton, 'From Virtuoso to Composer : Godowsky Featured in New Publications', *Musical America*, 2 June 1928, p. 32.

[9] 'Feste', 'Ad Libitum', *Musical Times* 81 (1940), p. 204.

give but one example. (By a strange turn of events, Engel—later the Editor of the *Musical Quarterly* and President of G. Schirmer—became a member of the Godowsky circle and the dedicatee of the left-hand Waltz Poems (1930).) Complaining of 'transcriptural obsessions in some musicians', he declared that 'one of the worst cases, undoubtedly, is that of Mr. Leopold Godowsky. He can not [*sic*] pick up a sheet of music, without wanting to trace over it convolutions of octave runs and double trills […], and all very cleverly, at that.'[10] Such wishful thinking—octave runs and double trills are actually rare in Godowsky's music—distracted attention from the broader issue at stake: Godowsky's reactionary musical language. To be sure, the *dernier cri* of the time was 'neoclassicism'. But this—actually highly elusive concept—had few points of contact with Godowsky's brand of arrangement: neoclassicism aimed at purging music of precisely the sort of anti-classical textures and procedures in which Godowsky gloried to his dying day. Godowsky was thus irrelevant to the brittle anti-Romantic modernism of the 1920s; moreover, much contemporary music was irrelevant to him. He had little time for 'ultra-modernists' (Berg's *Wozzeck*, for instance he damned as 'crazy' and 'dishonest');[11] his horizons did not extend much beyond Richard Strauss, Szymanowski (from whom he commissioned a concerto, which was never written), and early Bartók. Yet this is not to deny Godowsky's own modernist instincts; his addiction to arranging was in no small measure a symptom of his confidence in 'progress'. But his enthusiasm for the trappings of the 'modern' age—for cinemas, aeroplanes, science—reflected a 'rationalist' modernity that balanced confidence in innovation and progress with a respect for tradition. Godowsky owed allegiance to a world which, as the art historian Werner Haftmann put it, was characterized by 'a society which seemed to be within reach of its ideal—a life devoted to lofty aims in a world securely subjected to the control of man, at a time when the prevailing faith in technology, organisation, and progress seemed to have been justified by experience'.[12] That world, as Godowsky later came to realize, was in its death throes during his adult life.

The general stability of Godowsky's musical style is remarkable. Sure enough, there are changes of emphasis: within his arrangements, major trends include the diminishing appeal of structural surgery, a disinclination to rework melodies, and an increasing aversion from virtuosic effects such as glissandos, unmensurated flourishes, and cadenza figurations—devices not uncommon

in the earlier music (the paraphrase of Chopin's Waltz, Op. 18, even boasts a 'chromatic' glissando).[13] None the less, the axioms of his musical idiom were set early in his career. These stylistic traits include altered chords, to which Godowsky's distinctive chromatic and contrapuntal idiom owes a large debt; motivically concentrated textures; and a predilection, in arrangements, for vertically combining sections of the originals (or even superimposing two or more different pieces, as in Nos. 47 and 48 of the 'studies' on Chopin).

One hallmark of Godowsky's idiom is particularly evident in the arrangements: a certain restraint of approach, which the critic Adolph Brune termed 'discretion'.[14] As seen above, the later arrangements are generally conservative in their treatment of the original texts. Such fidelity in fact had its roots in the early artefacts. Godowsky's very first essay in arranging, the version of Chopin's Étude, Op. 25, No. 6, was 'strict' in its approach to the original musical materials and structure. The entire Chopin enterprise, in fact, was tarred with the brush of 'discretion'. In this sense, two broad types of work resulted from the first phase of arranging : the stricter, study arrangements (of Chopin's études, Henselt's 'Si oiseau j'étais', and Weber's Rondo from Op. 24) and the paraphrases (of Chopin's Opp. 16 and 18, Johann Strauss's waltzes, and Rameau and others in *Renaissance*). As the years clocked up, the radical paraphrase treatments lost their appeal, as did the study textures. Yet the 'strictness' inherent in the study 'type' persisted and became the structural premise of most of the later arrangements. The 1920s, in other words, saw the triumph of Godowsky's innate 'discretion'.

Stability and 'discretion': these, then, are two features of Godowsky's musical style. We may add another : *naïveté*. Admittedly, drawing parallels between Godowsky's art and the *opera* of 'naïve' painters such as Henri 'le Douanier' Rousseau (1844–1910) is problematic. To begin with, there is no readily available framework to sustain a rigorous, analytical comparison of the aesthetic qualities of the visual arts and music. Moreover, it would be misguided to argue that Godowsky was a naïve *composer* : this would suggest that he was largely untouched by contemporary culture and conventions, to posit that his work slips into a fairy-tale realm, to imply that he makes what Harold Rosenberg called a 'skilled use of unskill'.[15] But one can reasonably argue that there *are* naïve touches in his music, and that affinities do hold between Godowsky's circumstances and those of the naïve painter.

---

[10] 'Views and Reviews', *Musical Quarterly* 9 (1923), pp. 287–302 (p. 299).

[11] Godowsky, letter to Maurice Aronson, Vienna, 28 May 1931, quoted in Jeremy Nicholas, *Godowsky : The Pianists' Pianist* (Hexham, Northumberland, 1989), p. 147.

[12] *Painting in the Twentieth Century*, trans. Ralph Manheim and Janet Seligman (New York and Washington, 1965), vol. 1, p. 17.

[13] Godowsky stipulates that the glissando should be played with the second finger on the black keys and the fourth finger on the white keys.

[14] 'Godowsky's Chopin Studies: Technically and Aesthetically Considered', *Music* (Chicago) 17, no. 5 (February 1900).

[15] Review of *The Flowering of American Folk Art, 1776–1876*, exhibition catalogue by J. Lipman and A. Winchester, *New Yorker*, 25 March 1974, pp. 128–32, quoted in Roger Cardinal, 'Naïve Art', vol. 22 of *The Dictionary of Art*, ed. Jane Turner (London, 1996), pp. 439–42 (p. 440).

As mentioned above, Godowsky was largely self-taught as a composer, and the 'spontaneity' of naïve art is often attributed to such a lack of formal instruction. Though 'spontaneous' might not perhaps be the *mot juste* for Godowsky's art, certainly the young Godowsky was relatively uninhibited, a condition which is not far removed from that of 'spontaneity'. This youthful audacity—patent in his daring, for instance, to compile a mammoth set of Chopin arrangements—must have owed something to his not being immured at an early age in the trammels of musical orthodoxy. There are connexions, too, with the circumstances of naïve artists in Godowsky's artistic isolation and in the stability of his musical idiom. Naïve artists, after all, tend to stand aloof from contemporary artistic developments, drawing instead upon deeply ingrained patterns of thought, following established, trusted routines.

Haftmann identifies exaggeration, or accentuation, as a key component of naïve painting.[16] The naïve artist is fascinated by minutiae, with the exact definition of things, with selected representative details. In Godowsky this tendency is most apparent in the arrangements, which constantly magnify selected features of the originals: for instance, the sarabandes of *Renaissance* and the Bach 'elaborations' delight in projecting the second beat. Naïve, too, is the way Godowsky's alchemy rationalizes the originals—turning tonal sequences into real ones, tidying up phrase lengths, painstakingly rounding the forms, neatening the structural features. So is the compulsion to superimpose themes, as is the preoccupation with increasing the original textures' motivic density. In fact, for all the sophisticated veneer of Godowsky's works, one detects in them a subterranean *innocence*, Godowsky taking a pleasure in following a certain compositional drill. It is almost as if the familiar, tried-and-tested devices came to offer a comforting security; and it is perhaps for this reason that the tactics never palled.[17]

The first leaf of the holograph sketches for Godowsky's **Sonata**, held by the Library of Congress, is dated 30 August 1896. Fifteen years elapsed before the work was published. The delay may well have had something to do with Godowsky's array of musical commitments in the 1900s. A contributory factor was perhaps the scale of the work, the five movements of which total 1,182 bars (including repeats). But a further reason was submitted by Vernon Spencer, discussing the Sonata in the New York *Musical Courier* immediately prior to publication: Godowsky wanting his compositional skills to mature, he 'waited (following the example which he set himself and others as a pianist), till the master hand [was] everywhere in evidence'.[18] This suggests, then, that it was only in 1911, having just entered his forties, that Godowsky considered his apprenticeship in free composition over.

Godowsky 'advertised' his Sonata in the months preceding its publication by programming it in his recitals. (The version he performed may have deviated in some respects from the published score, given the evidence of the music examples—excerpts from proofs and autograph sources—in Spencer's article.) These performances elicited a mixed response. Though the critics generally warmed to Godowsky's playing, they generally tended to take his technical skill and interpretation for granted: the London *Daily Telegraph*, for example, casually asked 'What really humane parent is not gentle and solicitous in the treatment of his offspring?'[19] More column inches were devoted to the Sonata's length, technical demands, and involuted counterpoint, all of which proved to be controversial. However, the possibility of the Sonata's having any extra-musical significance received less attention. Though Godowsky did not issue a programme, Spencer held that 'a definite poetic thought stimulated [the Sonata's] conception', and he proceeded 'diffidently' to offer an 'outline'.[20] This synopsis merits attention, since many of Spencer's observations, not to mention his access to the proofs and autograph materials, suggest that he might have been privy to Godowsky's thoughts on the matter. Spencer's gist is this: 'Between the first and last movements lies an active life, the middle movements representing the *spirit* of various phases of the same'. The first movement...

...gives us glorious youth with life and the world unconquered ahead. Uncertainty and heroic impulse strive side by side. Youthful passion, into which the sensual element has hardly entered, the longing for the unattainable and the ideal all find expression. Yet all this 'Sturm und Drang,' all this certainty of final achievement, all this glow of passion, and all the beautiful sentiment of untried faith is hardly expressed, when, in the epilogue (in which the first thematic indications of the funeral march [of the final movement] appear), comes a premonition of death, the reminder of the transientness of earthly achievement and the nothingness of things material.[21]

[16] *Painting in the Twentieth Century*, vol. 1, p. 173.
[17] Godowsky's compositional style in relation to his arrangements is fully discussed in my 'The Arrangements of Leopold Godowsky : An Aesthetic, Historical, and Analytical Study', Ph.D. diss, University of Cambridge, England, 1997.
[18] 'Godowsky's E minor Sonata—I', *Musical Courier* (New York), 2 August 1911, p. 38.
[19] 30 January 1911, p. 5.
[20] 'Godowsky's E minor Sonata—II : Programmatical Sketch of the Sonata', *Musical Courier* (New York), 9 August 1911, p. 16.
[21] Ibid.

Contemporary critics were usually quick to spot the ghosts of Brahms and MacDowell haunting the rhapsodical, darkly heroic themes of this movement. Remarks on its broader structure were fewer in number, though. This has perhaps something to do with the movement's thematic bias, a preoccupation which led William S. Newman to suggest that the Sonata's form collapsed 'for want of perspective'.[22] Undeniably, Godowsky's structure is more concerned with generating a thematic argument, with constructing a narrative form, rather than with contriving a powerful, long-range tonal polarity. Indeed, the two principal keys, E minor and G major, associated with the two subject groups respectively, 'misbehave' by constantly stealing into areas that are (by convention) out-of-bounds in sonata form. That the first-subject themes are inexorably attracted to G, and the second-subject ones, to E minor, only encourages this tonal subversion. But *pace* Newman, a thematic bias cannot, by itself, cause the form to 'topple'. After all, much depends on the way the themes are handled and, indeed, on the aesthetic attitude of the listener ; in any case, the story of nineteenth-century music could be told in terms of the increasing impotence of tonality to generate forms. However, one aspect of Godowsky's structure does cause the form to lose 'perspective': the repeat of the exposition. This is, of course, easily remedied.

The first-subject group opens with a series of falling, sometimes rhythmically elusive, themes. Their irregular cut, the frequent halts, the quicksilver changes of dynamics—all these endow the music of the first two pages with a rhapsodic, conversational tone. Only from Tempo I does the music flow in regular phrases ; the sweeping tune here gives rise to music later recycled at the end of the movement, in the Epilogue. The second-subject group is shorter and consists of two elements: a confident, martial theme, soon dressed up in a semiquaver figuration typical of the later 'Java' Suite, and a rhythmically supple continuation. A fragment of the latter persists into the beginning of the development, where it joins forces with the Sonata's opening theme. Subsequently, the development rhythmically clarifies the theme first heard in bar 12, expatiates on two harmonic features of the exposition (namely its attraction to C minor harmony and whole-tone chords), and sketches a *scherzando* version of the martial theme. The section closes with the second-subject continuation. The ensuing recapitulation generally remains loyal to the scheme of the exposition, the main differences being its omission of some first-subject material

and elaboration of the martial theme with dreamier, more tranquil figuration, this theme being worked up to an apotheosis. The Epilogue then cools the temperature.

To return to Spencer's programme. 'The second movement symbolizes the time of love's fulfillment [*sic*], the time of peace and youthful happiness. The third and fourth the humor and joy of life itself with the senses tingling and awakened to pleasure'.[23] The *Andante cantabile*'s drooping lyricism and calm, poignant phrases are compelling in themselves. But they are much enriched by a certain unpredictability: in the course of presenting the three main themes, the music turns some unexpected corners; and it is this which secures the listener's undivided attention. The mood is lightened by the ensuing scherzo, originally entitled 'Intermezzo scherzando'. Its jaunty, skittish idiom carries many hallmarks of Godowsky's earlier style: study textures, flourishes, colourful augmented triads ; the opening gambit, with the single note tied over into subsequent bars, recalls the beginning of the third number of *Renaissance*, which arranges two minuets by Rameau. The tone is quietened by the fourth movement, an elegant, subtle waltz. Contemporary reviewers heard much Chopin in it ; indeed, the London *Daily News* sniffed that the movement 'might be considered original if Chopin had not existed'.[24] In fact, Godowsky's music takes its cue, not from Chopin, but from Johann Strauss and the light music of *fin-de-siècle* Vienna, and the resulting sentimental, more than faintly decadent waltz idiom—comprising gently altered chords, striking harmonic inflexions, delicate counterpoints, and lilting cross-rhythms—is one which Godowsky made unmistakably his own in *Walzermasken* and *Triakontameron*.

The fifth movement divides into four sections. The first, 'Retrospect', ruminates over themes from the first movement, though not in the order in which they initially appeared. The music has now adopted the past tense. 'Youth has grown old', suggests Spencer ; 'even the heroic second theme has lost its vigor and become quiet'.[25] But the backward glance serves a structural end, too. As in Beethoven's Ninth (and many other nineteenth-century works), the return of the themes aims at unifying the Sonata's broader design; at the same time it serves to shrink the time-scale between the first and last movements. After this brief reprise, the mood intensifies further, in the ensuing *Larghetto lamentoso* (the cello-and-piano version of which (1917) was performed at Godowsky's funeral). Spencer posited that 'the thought of earthly dissolution grows stronger' in this section, and that 'pious

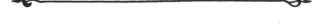

[22] *The Sonata Since Beethoven* (Chapel Hill, N. C., 1969), p. 420.
[23] 'Godowsky's E minor Sonata—II'.
[24] 30 January 1911, p. 5.
[25] 'Godowsky's E minor Sonata—II'.

reflections fill the soul'.[26] (The tone and context are not unlike those of the *arioso* prefacing—and later interrupting—the fugue from Beethoven's A♭ major piano sonata, Op. 110.) The *Larghetto*'s lyrical but flexible neo-Baroque phrases constitute a prelude to the ensuing fugue and supply many of the fugue's materials. In particular, its chromaticism lays the ground for the fugue subject, which presents the B-A-C-H motif in sequence and a continuation owing something to the left-hand part four bars from the end of the *Larghetto*. The countersubject is evolved entirely from the subject and even incorporates the B-A-C-H motif in inverted diminution. The episode following the three-part exposition places the B-A-C-H motif in counterpoint with its diminution (at *poco a poco più mosso, ma non troppo*) and develops the second phase of the subject (at *non legato*). There are middle entries from *molto tranquillo (a tempo)*. Most notable is the A-minor stretto section from ***p** dolce*. The subject enters in all three voices over a pedal-point on E; these statements overlap, the points of entry being spaced apart by one crotchet. When the key signature switches to E minor (the harmonic goal), the regular subject enters in stretto with the augmented subject. Meanwhile, the soprano sounds variants of the countersubject in diminution. Thus we hear the B-A-C-H motif in its regular form, in augmentation, and in inverted diminution simultaneously. All this culminates in the passage marked *stretto*, where two voices enter with the (unaltered) fugue subject just a quaver apart—no mean contrapuntal feat. The tension eases towards the end of the fugue, where the B-A-C-H motif is stated in its regular and inverted forms simultaneously. The final two bars of the fugue prepare the ostinato bass that reinforces the phrasal regularity of the next section, a funeral march (*Maestoso, lugubre*). The ostinato is in fact a free variant of the fugue subject, and marks a transitional stage in the subject's eventual transformation into the *Dies irae* plainchant from the Mass for the Dead. The *Dies irae* sounded, a calm E-major trio supervenes, which in Spencer's programme symbolizes the 'transfiguration'. It is this music which, after a brief reappearance of the *Trauerzug*, brings the hour-long odyssey to a hushed close.

While applying the finishing touches to the Sonata, Godowsky was occupied with a compositional project devoted entirely to the subject of the Sonata's fourth movement: the twenty-four *Walzermasken* (1912). Godowsky had a soft spot for the waltz, a genre that inspired him in every period of his composing career. In the case of *Walzermasken*, there was doubtless another

stimulus: the ambience of the 'Waltz City', Vienna, where between 1909 and 1914 Godowsky served as Imperial Professor of the *Klaviermeisterschule* of the Royal Academy of Music. The set met with a lukewarm critical response; but it did find a champion in the eccentric, and by then aged, pianist Vladimir de Pachmann. Were it not for *Walzermasken*, de Pachmann believed that he would have become a 'doddering old man, basking in the sun of [his] villa outside Rome'; he claimed to have 'escaped' this fate by religiously practising the nine numbers he had selected from the twenty-four every day.[27] Whatever the verity of his comments, de Pachmann was wise in making a selection; for though the work passes through many moods and textures, the variety lies within a narrow range. In fact, Godowsky acknowledged the length of the set and asserted that he had no objection to the performance of balanced selections. But for his own recitals he tended to programme the work in its entirety, in defiance of the critics' strictures. Given that the final number recalls the music of the first, the reason is obvious: Godowsky had constructed his set as a cycle and wanted to promote it as such.

Endowed with charisma and a certain *finesse*, the numbers of *Walzermasken* surely stand amongst Godowsky's finest free compositions. In the fashion of Brahms or Chopin, they play a host of metrical and phrasal tricks—consider 'Pastell (Fr. Sch.)', 'Skizze (Joh. Br.)', 'Tyll Ulenspegel', 'Légende', among others. Nearly all delight, too, in unexpected and expressive harmonic twists. Particularly beguiling are those numbers that gloss another composer's style: in the large part, they present a medley of musical quotations, leaving the listener to speculate on the often tantalizingly elusive sources. This can become quite an addictive game: not only are the sources always refracted through Godowsky's own stylistic lens, but, in addition, they are often too fleeting to be identified with confidence. And because the pastiches often vacillate between clearly citing a work and mimicking the composer's broader 'style', many of the 'quotations' seem to point to two or more works simultaneously. Take 'Skizze (Joh. Br.)'. Its general sound world is that of the *Liebeslieder* waltzes, and throughout it pokes fun at Brahms's penchant for hemiolas. But, more specifically, its opening recalls that of the Scherzo from the third piano sonata, Op. 5; later, the music seems to distort the final moments of the first movement of the G major violin sonata, Op. 78. The Liszt pastiche, 'Silhouette', similarly embeds specific quotations within the broader parody. Though it makes particular

[26] Ibid.

[27] *Musical Courier* (New York), 26 June 1924, quoted in Nicholas, *Godowsky*, p. 73.

mileage out of dramatic, rhapsodical gestures (characteristic, for example, of the 'Dante' Sonata or the Hungarian Rhapsodies), the opening is actually inspired by 'Orage', from the Swiss year of *Années de Pèlerinage*, while the ending parodies the final bars of 'Wilde Jagd', from the Transcendental Studies. And the 'Silhouette' is not the only number in *Walzermasken* to parody Liszt. 'Karikatur' initially sets forth a three-legged version of the opening of Liszt's 'Funerailles'; while 'Abendglocken', written on the twenty-fifth anniversary of Liszt's death, conjures up the world of 'Eglogue', again from the Swiss year of *Années de Pèlerinage*. The Chopinesque 'Profil' is especially subtle. It begins by suggesting Chopin's A♭ major Waltz, Op. 61, No. 1; later it distorts the contrasting idea of the B major Mazurka, Op. 56, No. 1—or is it quoting a passage from the A♭ major Waltz, Op. 64, No. 3; and the piece concludes by referring to the Étude, Op. 10, No. 2. But, in addition, 'Profil' throughout mimics Chopin's melodic idiosyncrasies : consider for instance the *fioritura*s, which intensify repeated melodies, or the passage-work, which often runs counter to the prevailing beat and metre. Chopin inspires other pieces as well. The suave 'Perpetuum mobile', for instance, owes much to the waltz interlude in the G minor Ballade and, to a lesser extent, the 'Two-Four' Waltz, Op. 42; it also seems to quote the A♭ major Étude, Op. 10, No. 10 at one point. Schumann's influence on *Walzermasken*, however, is slightly different from that of Chopin or Liszt. There are, of course, specific stylistic resonances, not only in 'Pastell (Fr. Sch.)', but also in 'Elegie' (the opening of which brings to mind the second number of *Davidsbündler*), 'Kontrast', and 'Satire'. But there is a more abstract influence: that on the set's conception, which is not unlike that of, say, *Davidsbündler* or *Carnaval*. This obligation is acknowledged by the title of the opening number, 'Karneval'. Finally, *Walzermasken* constantly conjures up the world of Johann Strauss—or, to be more precise, the world of Godowsky's 'symphonic metamorphoses' on Strauss. The music closing the set, for instance, distinctly resembles that signing off the paraphrase of *Wein, Weib und Gesang*. Even more redolent of the Strauss paraphrases is 'Humoresque', based on four notes that apparently embody the letters of a town in Saxony where one of Godowsky's early *inamorata*s lived.[28]

The title of the thirty-number *Triakontameron* (1919)—the other major collection of free compositions in three-four time—is quaint, even striking. Like Margaret of Angoulême's *Heptaméron*, it is inspired by Boccaccio's hundred-tale *Decameron* (or 'Ten Days' Work')—though, by my reckoning, had *Triakontameron* been constructed strictly along Boccaccio's lines, it would have comprised three hundred pieces. Its numbers are more intimate, less virtuosic, than those of *Walzermasken* and swear a stronger allegiance to the genre of the 'character' piece—a type perhaps most associated with Schumann, Grieg, and MacDowell; also evident is a certain hardening of Godowsky's stylistic arteries. Perhaps more significant, though, is the change of mood. An air of nostalgia for pre-War Vienna wafts freely through the collection, *Triakontameron* persistently evoking the ambience of the city that Godowsky abandoned in 1914 for the United States. A fitting sub-title for the work could be Godowsky's wistful remark on the aura surrounding his Viennese possessions: 'What has been, will and can never be again.'[29] In this respect, the individual titles speak volumes: 'Yesteryear…', 'The Salon', 'Memories', 'Terpsichorean Vindobona' ('Vindobona' being the Latin name for Vienna), 'Resignation', 'Lament', and 'Alt-Wien', the last of which reflects on the city 'Whose Yesterdays look backwards with a Smile through Tears'. The lilting waltz rhythms (especially prominent in 'The Temptress', 'Rendezvous', 'Sylvan Tyrol', 'An Epic', and 'Paradoxical Moods'), the drooping melodic contours, the yearning appoggiaturas, the expressive, chromatic inner parts—all these collude to secure the pensive, retrospective mood. Along the way, some objects become drawn into this nostalgic contemplation: namely 'The Music-Box' and 'The Cuckoo Clock'.

The character piece is well suited to evoking the 'otherness' of past but remembered times. By extension, it is also adept at calling up the 'otherness' of remote places. This is another concern of *Triakontameron* : witness 'Nocturnal Tangier' (inspired by a visit nearly a decade and a half earlier), 'Ethiopian Serenade', and 'Whirling Dervishes'. Godowsky's curiosity in non-Western cultures was long-standing. It was hinted at in *Walzermasken* ('Orientale') and in the *Miniatures* for piano duet (1918); it later gave rise to the 'Java' Suite. But Godowsky's interest in the exotic sheds light on another aspect of *Triakontameron*: its depiction of American scenes. For, despite his U.S. citizenship, Godowsky was none the less a native of Europe, and things American stoked his imagination nearly as much as things exotic. Just after completing *Triakontameron*, he remarked : 'Since I have become an American, and have made America my home, I find my Americanism expressing itself in my composi-

---

[28] See Nicholas, *Godowsky*, pp. 72–73.
[29] Godowsky quoted in Rosa Widder, letter to Paul Howard, 14 September 1934.

ATF122

tions',[30] and he later stated his intention to compose a 'travelogue musical picture of America'. This would ...

> ...begin with a polyphonic sketch entitled The 'Melting Pot' in which early America is shown as a combination of Old World elements. There will be a skyscraper movement to denote the energy and power of America and its significant aim to reach the skies. A description of Niagara Falls will symbolize the momentum of American life, and there will be local descriptions involving the Negro rhythms of the South and the Indian color of the West. Such elements as the cowboy and miner will be treated carefully. The final sketch will be my conception of glorified jazz.[31]

Indeed, in 1927 he was spotted—and photographed—on a New York hotel roof, studying the hum and clash of city traffic for a musical depiction.[32] The 'travelogue', though, never materialized, and, of his published output, only *Triakontameron* translates Godowsky's impressions of America into musical thought. 'The Enchanted Glen' depicts the shadows and lights in the Watkins Glen gorge, near Ithaca, New York; the 'Whitecaps' are those of Puget Sound, Washington, on a windy day. The 'Little Tango Rag' hints at Godowsky's growing interest in jazz; while the 'American Idyl', Godowsky noted, is an 'essay in American piano romanticism'.[33] There are also American resonances in the rather MacDowellian titles 'An Old Ballade' and 'An Epic'.

Some numbers of *Triakontameron* link *topoi*. The Viennese and American strands intertwine in the final number, 'Requiem (1914–18) : Epilogue', which commemorates the Great War, the piece culminating in a stirring arrangement of 'The Star-Spangled Banner'. The exotic and American elements come together in 'Ethiopian Serenade', Godowsky remarking enigmatically that 'the old colored mammy who cooked for me while in Seattle, where I wrote it, seemed to think it was the real thing'.[34] It should be added that each volume of *Triakontameron* supplies a good mix of the various topics. This is surely not by chance but by design, given Godowsky's concern for balance in any selection from *Walzermasken* and that the numbers of *Triakontameron* are *not* ordered according to their dates of composition.

The proposed American 'travelogue' was intended to be one of many, collectively to be known as *Phonoramas* or 'Tonal Journeys'. Always eager to broaden his horizons, Godowsky toured as far afield as South America, the Far East, South Asia, and North Africa. He considered travel not only a way of lifting the creative intellect,

but also a philosophical, spiritual enterprise, a way of advancing one's journey of self-discovery. The *Phonoramas*, then, sought to depict the places and peoples that Godowsky had encountered on his far-flung voyages. In so doing, they also aspired to 'eliminate the cheap claptrap endings to programs, [which send] the audience away with a little melodramatic excitement'.[35] The plan was ambitious. Initially the subjects were to be unashamedly exotic, and were to include Java, Japan, China, India, and Turkey, with Jewish- and Negro-inspired numbers thrown in. Godowsky later narrowed the selection to Java, Egypt, Assyria, Palestine, and America, as well as several unspecified European countries. In the event, though, the project did not progress beyond the **'Java' Suite** (1925). 'A visit to Java is like entering another world or catching a fleeting glimpse of immortality', enthused Godowsky ; 'musically, it is amazing. One cannot describe it because it is a simple sensation as difficult to explain as color to a blind person.'[36] Godowsky was not alone in having been seduced by the sounds of the gamelan, the traditional Javanese musical ensemble. Debussy's contact with it in 1889, at the Grand Universal Exhibition in Paris, is well known; later Britten was to recreate its sonorities in the ballet *The Prince of the Pagodas* (1956). Like Debussy, Godowsky had visited the 1889 Exhibition; like Britten, he had first-hand acquaintance with the musical tradition, having toured Java in 1923. None of the numbers of the Suite was composed on location, though: Godowsky's recital schedule in the Far East was remarkably punishing, and in any case he was in the thick of composing the Bach 'elaborations' at the time. Rather, the 'Java' Suite was written in the more comfortable conditions of Berlin, New York, Chicago, and Evanston in the winter of 1924–25—quite some time after the Far Eastern expedition of 1922–23. Neither did Godowsky transcribe the two Javanese melodies, *Gending Krawitan* and *Gending Kanjut*, found in 'Hari Besaar' ; rather, his source was Paul J. Seelig's collection of Javanese melodies entitled *Gending Djawi*.[37]

Godowsky was keen to own that the numbers of the Suite expressed his 'impressions in the native music-idiom' as he 'understood it'. The basis of the 'Java' Suite's music remains tonal, and the compositional resources include such 'Western' techniques as invertible counterpoint and fugue—often operating within rounded forms unknown to gamelan music. It was with acumen, then, that the London *Times* in 1927 judged the numbers of the Suite as '*bravura* studies in the modern manner touched with

[30] Godowsky in the *Musical Observer*, 5 May 1920, quoted in Nicholas, *Godowsky*, pp. 107–8.

[31] Godowsky quoted in Gdal Saleski, *Famous Musicians of a Wandering Race: Biographical Sketches of Outstanding Figures of Jewish Origin in the Musical World* (New York, 1927), p. 317.

[32] 'Piacevole', 'Heard in the Interval', *Musical Mirror*, December 1927, p. 275.

[33] Godowsky in the *Musical Observer*, 5 May 1920, quoted in Nicholas, *Godowsky*, p. 108.

[34] Ibid.

[35] Godowsky, quoted in Saleski, *Famous Musicians*, p. 317.

[36] Ibid., p. 318. For a little background see also Charles Hopkins, 'Godowsky's "Phonoramas" : A 20th-century "Wanderlust"', *Musical Times* 130 (1989), pp. 400–3.

[37] Bandoeng, 1922.

picturesque orientalism'.[38] Yet the work nevertheless skilfully evokes gamelan sonorities, not only in the first number, 'Gamelan', but also in other passages, for instance in 'A Court Pageant in Solo', 'In the Kraton', and the third of the 'Three Dances'. The strategy generally entails plotting a skeletal melody (in Javanese terminology, the *balungan*) through a stratified, motor-driven texture, with elaborations of this melody sounding simultaneously at a quicker pulse. The varied melody often seems to assume the role of the bronze kettles (*bonang*) which in gamelan music typically sound in syncopation with each other (as in the fourth and fifth bars of 'In the Kraton'). Meanwhile, evocations of gongs (*pencon*) regulate the flow, sometimes idiomatically stressing the second and fourth beats of the bar (as in the first bar of 'In the Kraton'). As Godowsky notes in his preface, the chromatic levels vary; but the pentatonic scale—which suggests the Javanese *slendro* scale—controls much of the harmony and melody. Many pentatonic complexes are due to the added seconds and sixths of Godowsky's harmonies or to the substitution of the fourth for the third of the triad; others can be reduced to stacks of fourths or fifths. Fourths are particularly important: they play a significant role in 'In the Kraton', while in 'Chattering Monkeys at the Sacred Lake of Wendit' they generate not only much of the harmony but also the melody. However, the pentatonic segments do often allow 'chromatic' (that is, non-pentatonic) inflexions. There is a whole-tone passage (from which fourths are necessarily banished) in 'In the Streets of Old Batavia'; this prefaces a melismatic 'Arab' section, which is in the Dorian mode. By contrast, the first of the 'Three Dances' is entirely Aeolian.

The textures of the 'Java' Suite are wide ranging. Some movements project an aural haze of neutralized chromaticism, evoking in their concern for sonority the sound worlds of Debussy and Ravel, even that of late Liszt. Examples include 'The Gardens of Buitenzorg', 'The Ruined Water Castle at Djokja', and 'Boro Budur in Moonlight'. Other textures experiment with stasis: the melodies of 'Boro Budur' and 'In the Kraton', for instance, repeat continually against a shifting kaleidoscope of background figurations, a tactic which recalls again the musical language of the gamelan. Other numbers race forward, their momentum often being generated by complementary rhythm: 'Chattering Monkeys' and 'Hari Besaar' are two examples.

Godowsky found the sonorities of the gamelan 'weird, spectral, fantastic, and bewitching'.[39] With some allowance for the context, much the same could be said of the sonorities of the 'Java' Suite. One can only wonder at the stimulus that Javanese music afforded Godowsky—an inspiration which impelled him to pen one of the most astonishing works of his career. 'On listening to this new world of sound I lose my sense of reality', Godowsky explained; 'it is the ecstasy of such moments, possible only through world travel, that makes life full of meaning and raises art to the pedestal of the Golden Age.'[40]

There is nothing remotely exotic about the forty-four variations, cadenza and fugue that make up the **Passacaglia** (1928). The work commemorated the centenary of Schubert's death, its subject being the first eight bars of the 'Unfinished' Symphony. Though Godowsky's 'Prefatory Remarks' on the work strike a suitably reverential tone—this was not the place to impugn Schubert's compositional skills—an interview for the New York *Musical Courier* in the centenary year revealed the extent of Godowsky's reservations. 'Hardly a long composition of Schubert exists which is not marred by page after page of loosely written and inferior work', he averred, continuing:

> Schubert did not know when to stop. [...] His creative faculty was so great and his fund of ideas so unlimited that he had no time to reflect and criticise like other composers whose ideas did not come so fast or so plentifully. His critical faculties were like a young and inexperienced gardener in a huge garden which grew flowers, vegetables, and weeds in boundless profusion. The kindest thing an older and judicious musician could do for Schubert would be to gather the flowers and throw out the weeds from his works.[41]

Indeed, Godowsky favoured a cut-and-paste method for 'enhancing' Schubert's piano sonatas. This entailed selecting the 'best parts from the best movements of the many sonatas and transposing and assembling them to make three or four superlatively excellent sonatas'.[42] One hardly dares to imagine the hue and cry had Godowsky chosen to mark the Schubert centenary with such a project; it is as well that the Passacaglia took priority.

The critic Clarence Lucas compared the Passacaglia to 'a kind of Polar expedition which very few travelers [sic] can undertake', adding that 'its label should be Ne Plus Ultra, for beyond these frontiers of harmony, counterpoint, structure, and technical difficulties, who will venture?'[43] Such remarks seem overstated today: though the work is technically strenuous, it lies well within the

---

[38] *The Times* (London), 28 February 1927, p. 10.
[39] Godowsky, quoted in Saleski, *Famous Musicians* p. 318.
[40] Ibid.

[41] Lucas, 'A Chat with Godowsky'.
[42] Ibid.
[43] Ibid.

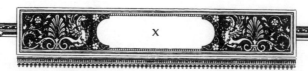

grasp of any modern pianist worth his salt. However, the work does present formidable *musical* challenges. The primary one issues from its treatment of Schubert's theme. In the 'Unfinished', the theme is harmonically open; in the Passacaglia it has gained a dominant upbeat and a perfect cadence. The resulting attention drawn to the theme's outer edges and the decision to retain its eight-bar phrasing (the final bar or two could easily have been snipped off) create a problem, that of smoothing the boundaries between the variations, of avoiding a 'stop-go' procession of short-winded phrases and regular cadences. Godowsky's tactics include maintaining the texture and figuration of one variation in the next (consider Nos. 1 and 2), undermining the final cadence (as in Variations 3 and 12), evolving a variation from a variation, and developing peripheral ideas through a sequence of variations. The performer, too, can lend a hand in this respect. Though Godowsky asks that the theme stand out in all variations, some judicious camouflaging would not go amiss. At the same time, the pianist could mould the variations into larger groups, and regulate the flow so as to downplay the eight-bar periods—a length which reigns supreme in all variations, save for the variations in diminution, and Nos. 25 and 34, which extend the cadence. (The sub-phrases are sometimes more intricate, though. Variation 1, for instance, plots a succession of two-bar members over the theme's three-bar units.)

The theme is treated in four ways. As in the first seven variations, it might serve as the bass line, as the harmonic anchor. A different tactic is evident in Variations 7 to 12, which locate the theme in the treble, enabling the harmonizations to become freer and elevating the general register. The third is to entrust the theme to an inner part : consider the dirge-like Variation 13, in which the theme sounds over a dotted-rhythm tonic pedal. The final method entails elaborating or developing the theme, as in Variation 19.

The argument proceeds in five phases, and these are largely articulated by the different treatments of the theme. The first phase is preoccupied with linear, chromatic textures, the theme serving as the bass line, and lasts until Variation 7. In the second, between Nos. 7 and 15, the theme acquires melodic prominence. Towards the end of this phase, the register sinks, all the better to signal the start of the momentum-building third phase (Nos. 16 to 27); this might be understood as the first 'development'. Initially articulated by the return of the theme to the bass (as at the beginning), its music makes full use of the key-

board range and indulges in much unbroken semiquaver motion. Variations 28 to 34 give the second development: the pulse decelerates and the music returns to the more measured chromaticism of the opening. However, the treatment of the theme becomes even more adventurous: Variations 31 to 33 transmit the theme in *scherzando* rhythmic diminution, while the ensuing variation crafts an ostinato figure from the first five notes of the theme (including the upbeat). The final phase supplies a suitably grandiose conclusion, and begins with Variation 35, in which the theme sounds once again in the bass (it was last located here in Variation 16).

Though the variations never transpose the theme, they do occasionally slip into the major mode. Variations 9 and 10 are in the relative major, D, and Variations 22 and 23 mark the halfway stage by migrating to the tonic major. A figure prominent in these B major variations was first heard in the sixth bar of Variation 10. Other variations, however, establish links reaching beyond the frontiers of the present movement: for instance, the canon (at one bar's distance) of Nos. 28 and 29 anticipates the canon (at the more manageable distance of two bars) near the end of the Fugue. Likewise, the Cadenza is prepared by the diminutions of the theme in Variations 9 (which contracts the theme above the *cantus firmus*), 31, 32, and the closing variations (from No. 42 onwards), as well as by the diminutions of the theme that sometimes chaperon the subject's final long notes, as in Variations 16, 36, and 41.

The variations sometimes allude to other composers' works or styles. Variation 41 suggests the opening of the slow movement of Schubert's F minor Fantasia for piano duet. Variation 38 takes its cue from the piano figuration of 'Erlkönig'. Number 35 has an affinity with the tenth of Brahms's 'Handel' Variations. The phrasal foreshortenings of the final variations suggest the *Prestissimo* section near the end of Grieg's Ballade, Op. 24. And one can always detect something of Rachmaninov's manner in Godowsky's chromatic and contrapuntal inflexions and occasional modal colourings.

In particular, the Passacaglia constantly invokes the spirit of Bach. This is due not only to its contrapuntal bias, but also to the organ-like sonorities which it favours and, of course, its very title and form. For Godowsky these references to Bach and his sound world brought about the requisite weighty, monumental tone that he judged suitable for a homage—even if it were to Schubert. The sonorities of Variations 12 and 35 are particularly organ-

like; notice also the 'pedal' entry of the subject in the fifth system of the Fugue and the solid textures of the final page. Other indicators of 'monumentality' include the *tierces de Picardie*, the final plagal cadence, and the numerous pedal-points.

The Fugue is far from being a textbook specimen. The four-part exposition, for instance, has some unconventional elements, which are to do with the pattern of subject entries and the shape of the 'answer'; later Godowsky loosens and adapts the counterpoint at his pleasure. The subject is the earlier Passacaglia theme, but with a short chromatic continuation which makes it open-ended, and which supplies countersubject material. Having passed through a hemiola, the music presents an eight-bar episode, after which it states the theme again (now in D major), though not in its extended, fugal form but in the closed version used by the Variations. More entries follow, in E minor, E major (with a hint of stretto), and A minor; in the process the theme regains its fugal attributes. Another short episode intervenes, before the subject appears, *maestoso*, in a luminous C major. It is not long before the regular subject is superimposed onto its augmented form, in E minor, and all this prefaces a canon at two bars' distance, in the tonic. Particularly noteworthy is the music over the final tonic pedal, from twelve bars before the end. Above an attenuated statement of the subject, Godowsky plots the theme that *follows* the introductory figure of Schubert's 'Unfinished'. At this point, the work has begun to overflow its boundaries, and the music must come to an end.

Photo 1: Leopold Godowsky

The Cadenza (which Godowsky revised in later years, though his alterations are now lost) is altogether more 'pianistic' in tone, and is sandwiched between the Variations and the Fugue. Its highly chromatic harmonies might initially bewilder; but in fact, as the unbroken F♯ pedal indicates, they merely elaborate on the dominant. Though the theme does occasionally enter in full (albeit in diminution), it is the figure from the fifth and sixth bars of Schubert's theme which holds the stage; the left-hand part from the third bar of the Cadenza clearly shows this motif. However, its intervals slowly distort, so that by the seventeenth bar of the Cadenza (or so) the figure has come to relate to the second and third bars of the theme — but in inversion. The Cadenza, then, engages with Schubert's theme in a very different way from that of the adjacent Variations and Fugue; in a word, it analyses the thematic *structure*.

— Dr Millan Sachania
London, England, 1999

Photo 2: Leopold Godowsky, Albert Einstein, Arnold Schönberg

Godowsky : A Biographical Sketch

'Godowsky : the only musician of this age who has given a lasting, a real contribution to the development of piano music'.

— Sergei Rachmaninov[1]

'I call him the Brahma of the Keyboard'.

—James Gibbons Huneker[2]

Even during his own lifetime, when the musical scene boasted a luminous constellation of outstanding pianists, Leopold Godowsky (1870–1938) achieved a supremacy of the keyboard that the critic Harold C. Schonberg has called 'the most perfect pianistic mechanism of the period and very likely of all time'.[3] The American music critic, James Huneker noted that 'nothing like him, as far as I know, is to be found in the history of pianoplaying since Chopin. [...] He is a pianist for pianists, and I am glad to say that the majority of them gladly recognise this fact'.[4] Carl Flesch remembered seeing Josef Hofmann, Theodor Leschetizky, and Vladimir de Pachmann 'crowd round' Godowsky 'in the profoundest admiration while he played one of his Chopin arrangements, whose difficulties seemed wellnigh [*sic*] inconceivable even to these sovereign exponents of the instrument'.[5] Indeed, Hofmann once pronounced that Godowsky was 'the master of us all'.[6]

Born on 13 February 1870 in a small town outside Wilno, Poland, Leopold was the only child of Anna and Mathew Godowsky. Having shown musical aptitude but living in financial distress, Godowsky was invited to study music with his mother's friends, Louis and Minna Passinock. A violinist himself, Louis began teaching Godowsky the instrument, discouraging the boy from playing the piano to the point where Godowsky had to indulge his attraction to the keyboard secretly. As Passinock also ran a piano shop, this was not difficult, and Minna quietly taught the young

Photo 3: Leopold Godowsky, 9 years old.

Godowsky scales and rudimentary music theory. When Passinock heard Godowsky playing one of his youthful compositions at the piano, however, he decided that the boy's musical future lay with the keyboard. After that episode, Godowsky began to play everything that came his way, and Passinock, who had by now practically 'adopted' the child, began promoting the young prodigy to the point of exploitation.

Godowsky embarked on the first of several concert tours at the age of ten. With the support of a banker from Königsberg, a Herr Feinberg, he won entry into the Königliche Hochschule für Musik in Berlin, where he studied the piano with Ernst Rudorff. Godowsky could tolerate the institution for only three months, though, and fled, eventually departing Europe in order to tour America with Passinock in 1884. He returned to Europe in 1886, intending to study with Liszt; but word of the composer's death deflected Godowsky's path towards the home of Camille Saint-Saëns in Paris. Rapidly, Godowsky became Saint-Saëns's protégé, and in time the French composer expressed his wish legally to adopt the young pianist—on the condition that Godowsky assumed his name. (Godowsky demurred, much to Saint-Saëns's displeasure.) Though Saint-Saëns offered Godowsky little in the way of pianistic and compositional discipline, he did supply much encouragement, practical advice, and a valuable *entrée* into Parisian musical society: soon Godowsky was acquainted with musicians such as Fauré, Gounod, Massenet, Pierné, Widor, and Delibes.[7] After a spell play-

---

[1] Quoted in a proposal for an 'International Master Institute of Music', New York, 1934.

[2] *New York Times*, 27 April 1919.

[3] *The Great Pianists from Mozart to the Present*, rev. edition (New York, 1987), p. 336.

[4] *Unicorns* (London, [1919]), pp. 180-81.

[5] *The Memoirs of Carl Flesch*, trans. Hans Keller (London, 1957), p. 201.

[6] See obituary of Godowsky, New York *Musical Leader*, 26 November 1938.

[7] See Jeremy Nicholas, *Godowsky : The Pianists' Pianist* (Hexham, Northumberland, 1989), p. 25.

ing in aristocratic London salons, Godowsky returned to the United States, in 1890. Six months later he became one of the first pianists to play in Carnegie Hall, two weeks before it officially opened; a week later he married; and the next day Godowsky became an American citizen.

During this time, Godowsky began to teach, first at the New York School for Music, and then at the Broad Street Conservatory in Philadelphia, where he became head of the piano department. Two years later, Godowsky acquired a similar but more prestigious post at the piano faculty of the Chicago Conservatory. By the late 1890s, then, his reputation as a complete musician—performer, composer, teacher—had steadily blossomed.

In 1900 he secured a year's leave from the Conservatory to advance his performing career in Europe. He stopped in Paris, Vienna, Dresden, and Leipzig before finding himself in Berlin. The thought of a recital there was truly intimidating: though his reputation had grown among pianists and teachers, he was all but unknown to critics and the public; moreover, his 'competition' constituted d'Albert, Busoni and Rosenthal. After spending two months absorbing the city's artistic atmosphere, Godowsky made his début on 6 December 1900 at the Beethoven-Saal, where he played concertos by Tchaikovsky and Brahms with the Berlin Philharmonic Orchestra, seven of his 'studies' on Chopin's études, and his arrangement of Weber's *Aufforderung zum Tanz*. By all accounts, Godowsky's impact on the audience, which was full of Berlin pianists and critics, was nothing short of sensational. In his review of the recital, Max Löwengard of the *Börsen-Zeitung* held that Godowsky 'is the greatest technician who has ever been heard, and at the same time he remains a good musician. This is a rarity'.[8] Godowsky himself reported:

Photo 4: Leopold Godowsky

The applause after the first movement [of the Brahms concerto] startled me. It was terrific. It took a long time before I could begin the second part. After the last movement I was recalled I don't know how many times. […] The success [of the Chopin arrangements] was greater than anything I have ever witnessed […]. To tell how many times I had to come out after the paraphrases would be impossible. I could not count them…. […]

I was told that almost all the critics stayed till the end—a very rare occurrence in Berlin, as they have to attend several concerts every evening and are so blasé that nothing interests them. The critic from the Boersen Zeitung (Lowewengard [*sic*]) applauded frantically—a thing no critic is supposed to do! Professor Taubert called at my house the following day to congratulate me personally. He is the most feared critic in Germany.

We get invitations to dinner everywhere; people stream to our house.[9]

'With one recital Godowsky had conquered the musical capital of the world and assured himself of a place among the great keyboard players of history', sums up his biographer Jeremy Nicholas; 'overnight he became one of the highest-priced of all instrumentalists'.[10] Thereafter, Godowsky settled in Berlin, touring all over Europe, Russia, North Africa, and Asia Minor. He left Berlin in 1909 to succeed Busoni as the Director of the *Klaviermeisterschule* of the Imperial Royal Academy of Music in Vienna, a post carrying a fat salary, generous tax-breaks and a host of perks. There he stayed until 1914, when the deteriorating political situation impelled him to flee to Great Britain and subsequently to New York.

Wherever it was located, Godowsky's base—be it his home or a *pied-à-terre* while on tour—became a centre of local artistic life. Godowsky's daughter Dagmar recalled that in New York 'it was not unusual to come home

---

8   December 1900, quoted in Nicholas, p. 51.
9   Letter to W. S. B. Matthews, 24 December 1900, quoted in Leonard Liebling, 'Variations', *Musical Courier* (New York), 15 December 1938.   10   *Godowsky*, p. 53.

and find Paderewski, Chaliapin, Kreisler, Hofmann, Caruso, Elman, Damrosch. Everyone from Auer to Zimbalist!'.[11] In Berlin, the crowd often included artists such as Leschetizky, de Pachmann, Busoni, Scriabin, and Kreisler; in Vienna, Mahler, Prokofiev, Thomas Mann, Oskar Straus and Franz Lehár; and in Los Angeles, Stravinsky, Gershwin, Rachmaninov, Heifetz, Casals, and Chaplin. 'No musician was more capable of constantly gathering around him creative companions in so many fields of artistic work', remembered Abram Chasins.[12] But that said, Godowsky's tailor or someone whom he had just met on the street might have been among the assembled company. Chasins noted that 'everyone and anyone was welcome' in the Godowsky household;

Photo 5: Leopold Godowsky

> there seemed to be a perpetual party going on. The table was always set and loaded with food and drink. Godowsky was a born host. […]. Popsy loved people and loved to be surrounded by them. If he invited you to come over 'just for a little quiet talk and music,' you might arrive to find twenty people who had just dropped in […]. Everyone was treated with equal informality and graciousness. Popsy's old-world courtesy and sparkling humor pervaded every word and action as he waddled between the living-room and adjacent dining-room filling plates and glasses, emptying ashtrays, scattering wry remarks and vicious gibes.[13]

Yet Godowsky's rigorous socialising rarely interfered with his composing. 'He stood up with an air of having just remembered something,' Chasins recalled of an event in New York:

Slowly he made his way to the corner of the room, leaned against the grand piano, reached for a pencil and manuscript paper, and began to write quickly. As we quieted down, the sudden silence seemed to distract him. Lifting his baby face and waving his left arm while he continued to make notes with his right, he said: 'Go on. Go on, I'll be finished soon. Please talk, play, eat something, drink something. Don't let me disturb you.' He worked steadily and intensely for a long time, never taking his eyes off his work. Eventually everyone but [pianist Mischa] Levitzki and I stole out. At last Popsy put his pencil down with an air of finality and looked around. In a surprised voice he asked: 'Where's everybody? Where did everybody go?' He seemed disturbed and hurt that they had left. 'They should know,' he said, 'that it doesn't bother me to have people. I've never had privacy. I never needed it. I always work with people around. A roomful of friends is the best condition for my work. All my life it has been so.'[14]

On occasion, though, even Godowsky found his hectic social life detrimental to compositional work. The stress of completing one particular project led to one of New York City's biggest missing-person searches in years.[15] In the fall of 1915, Godowsky was behind schedule to deliver thirty educational adaptations to the Arts Publishing Company of St Louis. Then living in New Jersey, Godowsky left for New York City one morning carrying $1,000 in cash. When he failed to return home that night, his wife Frieda alerted the police. Soon the *New York Times* headlines proclaimed 'GODOWSKY MISSING' and the press followed the case with scrutiny. The police retraced the pianist's steps; a Polish telepath held a séance by invitation of Godowsky's friends; a vaudeville theatre manager claimed that Godowsky was just about to join his company as an attraction. But no real progress was made until Godowsky wrote to his fam-

---

[11] Dagmar Godowsky, *First Person Plural: The Lives of Dagmar Godowsky* (New York, 1958), p. 29.
[12] *Speaking of Pianists…* . 3rd edition (New York, 1981), p. 27.
[13] Ibid., pp. 28–29.
[14] Ibid., pp. 36–37.
[15] The full story is told in Nicholas, *Godowsky* pp. 90-94.

ily from his hideaway in Hackensack, New Jersey, explaining that he was in 'voluntary exile' in order to secure the peace and quiet he needed for finishing the educational adaptations. He refused to reveal his precise location and to return home, however, until the work was completed.

Godowsky's career took him all over the world. The 1920s were particularly demanding on Godowsky in this respect, and in these years he toured Turkey, Mexico, South America, Japan, China, Hong Kong, Java, Singapore, the Philippines, Honolulu, North Africa, and Palestine. However, Godowsky suffered a series of calamities at the end of the decade which discouraged him from embarking on any further such exotic voyage. The 1929 Wall Street Crash wiped out much of his considerable fortune. In June 1930 Godowsky suffered a stroke during a recording session in London. This left his concert career in ruins, and he never played in public again. His younger son committed suicide in 1932; his wife died not long afterwards. Bereft and lonely, sick and forcibly retired, financially insecure and sickened by Europe's steep descent into political barbarism, Godowsky lost the will to compose. 'The world-conditions and my philosophy of life are so disturbingly gloomy that I find not the slightest joy in liv-

ing and am apathetic,' Godowsky wrote in 1936. 'Whatever I do I do it from a strong sense of duty and an irresistible urge for perfection. And so I am revising, editing, correcting and improving all my compositions.'[16] While shuttling restlessly to-and-fro Europe and America (a visit to Russia in 1935 ended prematurely, Godowsky leaving in disgust at the political climate), he drafted utopian plans for a 'World Synod of Music and Musicians' and an 'International Master Institute of Music' under his direction. But his spirits continued to sink. Two weeks before he died of cancer on 21 November 1938, Godowsky declared in a celebrated missive:

> I am in constant gloom, and my despair is growing daily, due to the unprecedented, barbaric happenings all over our little wobbly planet, happenings which make the Dark Ages seem like expressions of transcendental liberalism. And what is the future of our beloved music? Is the source of musical inspiration completely exhausted? Is all culture going to be with a 'K'? Where is Fate driving us to? Is this the Dusk of the Earth? Is the annihilation of all human achievements ahead of us?…When we allow o[u]r thoughts to deepen, life becomes unbearable.[17]

— *Edited by* Millan Sachania

Photo 6: Leopold Godowsky

[16] Letter to Paul Howard, New York, 19 September 1936.
[17] Letter to Leonard Liebling, 5 November 1938, Deal, N.J.

dedicated to my dear wife

Sonata in E Minor

for piano solo

ATF122

Sonata in E Minor

I.

Allegro non troppo, ma appassionato.

LEOPOLD GODOWSKY
(1870–1938)

ATF122

8

*)Der Autor rät, beim öffentlichen Vortrag die Wiederholung fortzulassen.

ATF122

17

II.

Andante cantabile.

27

ATF122

30

*vi-

p tranquillo
una corda

pp non troppo lento

-de   più sostenuto

pp espr.

perdendosi

III.

Allegretto vivace e scherzando.

IV.

Allegretto grazioso e dolce.

44

46

ATF122

V.

Retrospect
Lento, mesto

48

49

ATF122

50

Fuga
Molto espressivo (l'istesso tempo)

poco a poco più mosso, ma non troppo
espress.

molto cresc.

f
dim.
p cresc.

54

Maestoso, lugubre

p sempre marcato

sempre p

pp >

più p senza cresc.

p

sf

pp >

p

più p senza cresc.

p

sf

pp >

p

Maestoso, lugubre. (tempo I^{mo})

58

dedicated to Dr. Wilhelm Stekel

Walzermasken

24 Tonfantasien im Dreivierteltakt
(24 Character Pieces in Triple Meter)
for piano solo

1. Karneval [Carnival]
2. Pastell (Fr. Sch.)
3. Skizze (Joh. Br.) [Sketch]
4. Momento Capriccioso
5. Berceuse
6. Kontraste
7. Profil (Fr.Ch.)
8. Silhouette (Fr. L.)
9. Satire
10. Karikatur
11. Tyll Ulenspegel
12. Legende

13. Humoreske (über 4 Noten)
14. Französisch [French]
15. Elegie
16. Perpetuum mobile
17. Menuett
18. Schuhplattler
19. Valse macabre
20. Abendglocken (Angelus) [Evening Bells]
21. Orientale
22. Wienerisch [Viennese]
23. Eine Sage [A Tale]
24. Portrait (Joh. Str.)

The 24 character pieces of *Walzermasken* should be treated as a cyclic work composed of interrelated pieces. However, the composer has no objection if any of the pieces are presented in concert in any arbitrary ordering. Of course, it is advisable that such a selection intermixes pieces of differing characters, simply to avoid monotony. For example, cheerful pieces would better follow somber ones, and pieces in fast tempos would better follow those in slower tempos, and such like. Because the entire work lasts one hour if played without interruption, it is recommended that if the 24 pieces are presented in a single concert, the order in this publication be followed. Additionally, long pauses should follow the conclusions of pieces No. 8 (*Silhouette*) and No. 16 (*Perpetuum mobile*).

It is of the greatest significance to devote careful attention to the use of the damper pedal. As a general rule, bass notes, chords and inner voices that cannot be sustained with the right or left hand can be compensated for with the pedal, in which the length of each note should correspond to the notated duration for pedal. Additionally, bass notes, whose durations are not indicated precisely as a result of a simpler notational style, should remain sounding, except, of course, if a specific staccato touch is requested. For a model example of an acute use of the damper pedal, see No. 20 (*Abendglocken*), in which the complete mood and character of the piece depend on abundant and intelligent pedaling. The composer has expressed his opinions on the complex art of pedaling in his Study No. 45 on the Chopin Études in a concise, yet thorough manner.

1. Karneval
[Carnival]

LEOPOLD GODOWSKY
(1870–1938)

Maestoso, con brio ♩.= 60-66

2. Pastell

(Fr. Sch.)

LEOPOLD GODOWSKY

66

3. Skizze
(Joh. Br.)
[Sketch]

LEOPOLD GODOWSKY

4. Momento Capriccioso

LEOPOLD GODOWSKY

5. Berceuse

LEOPOLD GODOWSKY

6. Kontraste

LEOPOLD GODOWSKY

7. Profil

(Fr. Ch.)

LEOPOLD GODOWSKY

Moderato

ATF122

8. Silhouette

(Fr. L.)

LEOPOLD GODOWSKY

Allegro impetuoso

85

ATF122

9. Satire

LEOPOLD GODOWSKY

88

ATF122

10. Karikatur

LEOPOLD GODOWSKY

11. Tyll Ulenspegel

LEOPOLD GODOWSKY

12. Legende

LEOPOLD GODOWSKY

13. Humoreske
(über 4 Noten)

LEOPOLD GODOWSKY

Vivace (doppio movimento)

rall. _ _ _ _ dolce e leggiero

p dolce espr.

sempre espr.

sf sf

14. Französisch
[French]

LEOPOLD GODOWSKY

Moderato e grazioso

15. Elegie

LEOPOLD GODOWSKY

Molto moderato

Tempo I

sempre p

rall.-

mesto e rall.

16. Perpetuum mobile

LEOPOLD GODOWSKY

17. Menuett

LEOPOLD GODOWSKY

D.C. al Fine
senza repetizione.

18. Schuhplattler

LEOPOLD GODOWSKY

*) Die Takte von A bis B können wiederholt werden.

118

*) Auch die nächsten 24 Takte (bis zum Schluss) können zweimal gespielt werden.

ATF122

19. Valse macabre

LEOPOLD GODOWSKY

20. Abendglocken

(Angelus)

[Evening Bells]

LEOPOLD GODOWSKY

124

sempre pp

più moderato

rall. e dim.

Zum 25. Todestag von **Franz Liszt**
31. Juli 1911. Ischl.

ATF122

21. Orientale

LEOPOLD GODOWSKY

22. Wienerisch
[Viennese]

LEOPOLD GODOWSKY

23. Eine Sage
[A Tale]

LEOPOLD GODOWSKY

24. Portrait

(Joh. Str.)

LEOPOLD GODOWSKY

*) Mit diesen Takte hört das Portrait (Joh. Str.) auf und Reminiscenzen aus dem Karneval (Walzermasken No 1) erklingen.

Triakontameron

Thirty Moods and Scenes in Triple Meter
(in six volumes)
for piano solo

ATF122

1. Nocturnal Tangier

LEOPOLD GODOWSKY
(1870–1938)

Seattle, August 25th, 1919

2. Sylvan Tyrol

LEOPOLD GODOWSKY

Allegretto grazioso ♩ = 132-144

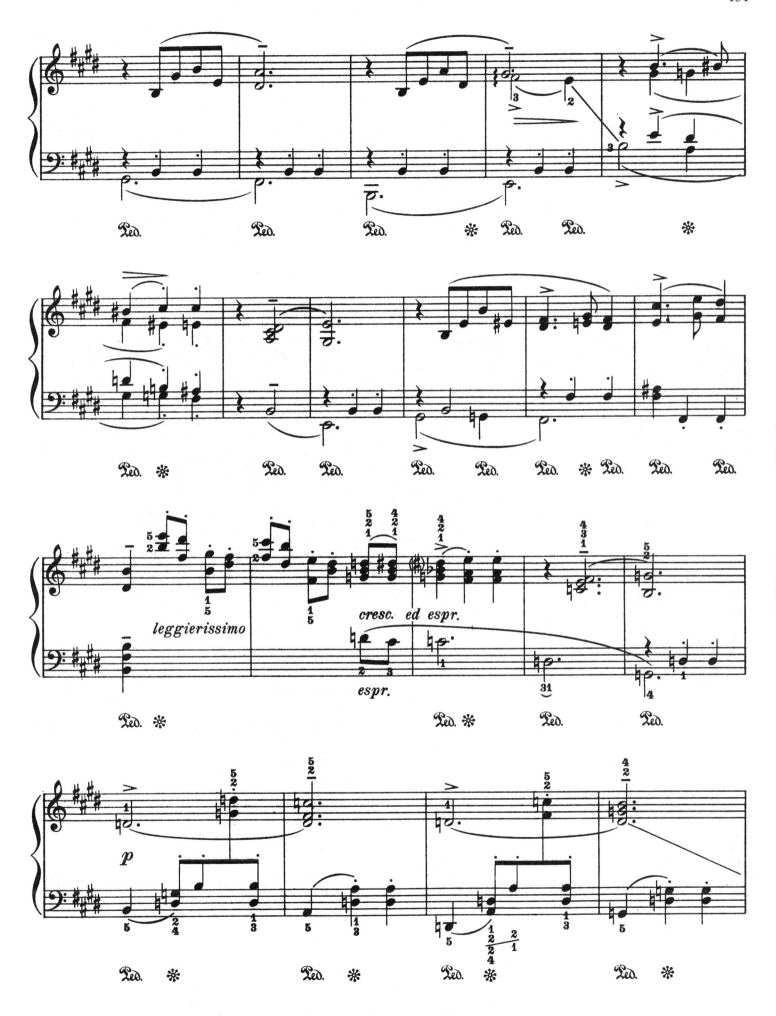

152

Seattle, August 7th, 1919

ATF122

3. Paradoxical Moods

LEOPOLD GODOWSKY

Allegro con brio ♩. = 84-92

Seattle, August 10th, 1919

4. Rendezvous

LEOPOLD GODOWSKY

Allegretto lusingando ♩= 144 - 160

New York, February 5th, 1920

5. Twilight Phantasms

LEOPOLD GODOWSKY

164

165

ATF122

perdendosi

poco rall.

Seattle, August 12th, 1919

6. The Pleading Troubadour

LEOPOLD GODOWSKY

Seattle, August 23rd, 1919

7. Yesteryear...

LEOPOLD GODOWSKY

174

Tempo Iº ♩ = 104 - 112

Los Angeles, October 13th, 1919

ATF122

8. A Watteau Paysage

LEOPOLD GODOWSKY

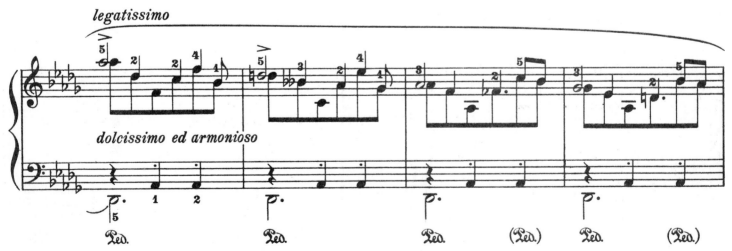

Seattle, August 10th, 1919

ATF122

9. Enchanted Glen

LEOPOLD GODOWSKY

182

New York, January 8th, 1920

10. Resignation

LEOPOLD GODOWSKY

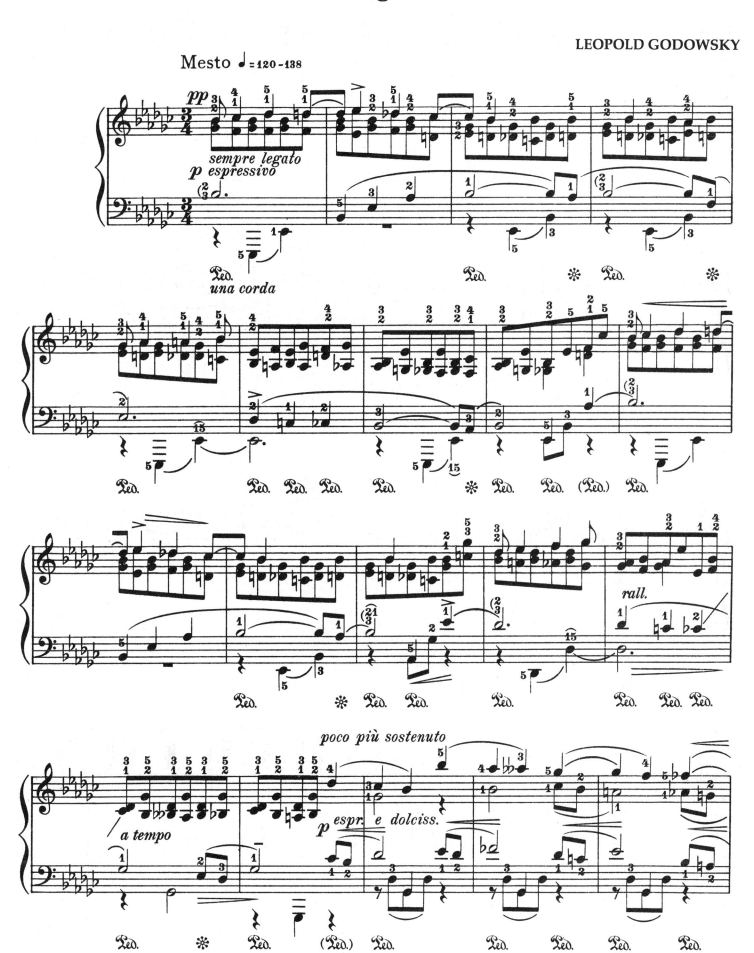

184

ATF122

186

New York, January 14th, 1920

ATF122

11. Alt-Wien

"Whose Yesterdays look backwards
with a Smile through Tears."

LEOPOLD GODOWSKY

Andante lusingando ♩ = 120 - 132

p con sentimento

sostenuto

mf

a tempo

sostenuto

a tempo

p

molto

189

ATF122

Seattle, August 8th, 1919

12. Ethiopian Serenade

LEOPOLD GODOWSKY

poco rall.

p espr.

pp poco più sostenuto

perdendosi

pp

Seattle, August 22nd, 1919

ATF122

13. Terpsichorean Vindobona

LEOPOLD GODOWSKY

Tempo Iº

200

ATF122

Seattle, August 14th, 1919

14. Whitecaps

LEOPOLD GODOWSKY

204

Seattle, August 24th, 1918

ATF122

15. The Temptress

LEOPOLD GODOWSKY

Seattle, August 11th, 1919

16. An Old Ballade

LEOPOLD GODOWSKY

una corda

meno mosso
molto tranquillo

Seattle, August 16th, 1919

17. An American Idyll

LEOPOLD GODOWSKY

Andante pastorale ♩.= 46-52

ATF122

Seattle, August 27th, 1919

18. Anachronisms

LEOPOLD GODOWSKY

216

Seattle, September 3rd, 1919

19. A Little Tango Rag

LEOPOLD GODOWSKY

Seattle, August 26th, 1919

20. Whirling Dervishes

LEOPOLD GODOWSKY

Più mosso

Los Angeles, October 16th, 1919

ATF122

21. The Salon

LEOPOLD GODOWSKY

Allegretto languido ♩. = 44-50

p grazioso ed espressivo

mf espressivo

p

dim.

p

228

ATF122

230

Los Angeles, October 27th 1919

ATF122

22. An Epic

LEOPOLD GODOWSKY

232

ATF122

Tempo I°

238

Chicago, January 30th, 1920

ATF122

23. The Music Box

LEOPOLD GODOWSKY

* With the exception of the few *sf* tones, the entire composition is to be played extremely *pp*.

poco più sostenuto

Seattle, August 31st, 1919

ATF122

24. Lullaby

LEOPOLD GODOWSKY

244

Seattle, August 17th, 1919

ATF122

25. Memories

LEOPOLD GODOWSKY

Ancor un poco più mosso

250

Los Angeles, October 18th, 1919

ATF122

26. The Cuckoo Clock

LEOPOLD GODOWSKY

252

Seattle, August 28th, 1919

ATF122

27. Lament

Andante mesto ♩ = 88-104

LEOPOLD GODOWSKY

254

Seattle, August 19th, 1919

ATF122

28. Quixotic Errantry

LEOPOLD GODOWSKY

260

ATF122

Seattle, August 18th, 1919

29. Poëme Macabre

LEOPOLD GODOWSKY

Los Angeles, October 21st, 1919

30. Requiem (1914-1918): Epilogue

LEOPOLD GODOWSKY

Largo lugubre ♩ = 56-66

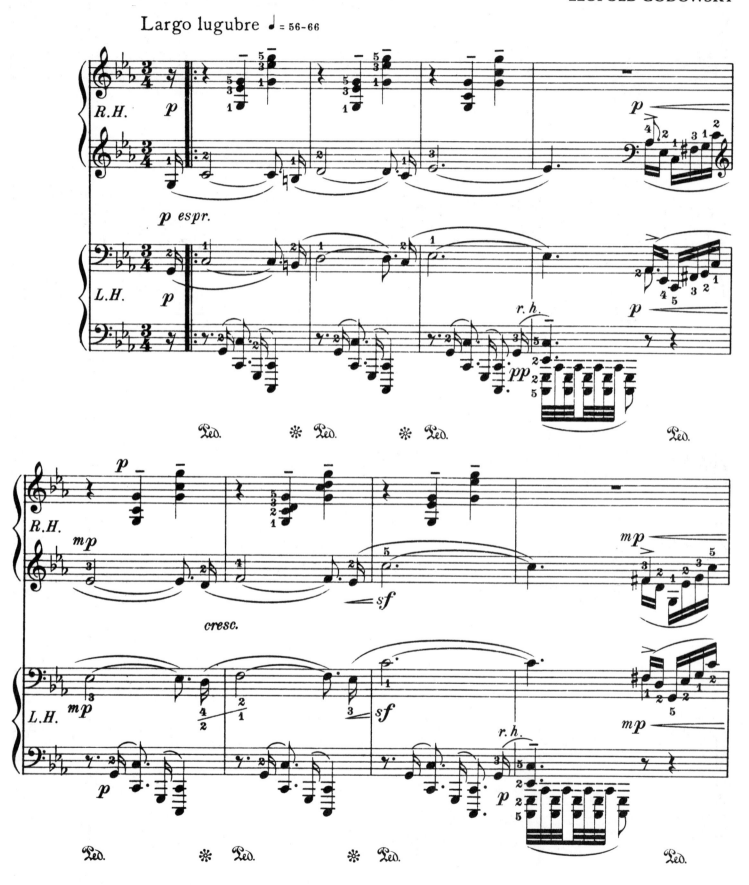

270

ATF122

Maestoso (♩ = 66-76)

272

Grandioso

allargando
molto cresc.

ff

tre corde

ATF122

Los Angeles, October 24th, 1919

ATF122

to my friend J. Campbell Phillips

Java Suite

(in four parts)
for piano solo

ATF122

Duration Schedule
Approximate Duration of Each Number and Each Part

Part I (ca. 10 ½ minutes)
1. Gamelan - ca. 3 minutes
2. Wayang-Purwa – ca. 3 ½ minutes
3. Hari Besaar – ca. 4 minutes

Part II (ca. 8 ½ minutes)
4. Chattering Monkeys at the Sacred Lake of Wendit – under 2 minutes
5. Boro Budur in Moonlight – ca. 3 ½ minutes
6. The Bromo Volcano and the Sand Sea at Daybreak – ca. 3 minutes

Part III (ca. 12 minutes)
7. Three Dances – under 5 ½ minutes
8. The Gardens of Buitenzorg – ca. 3 ½ minutes
9. In the Streets of Old Batavia – over 3 minutes

Part IV (ca. 12 minutes)
10. In the Kraton – over 5 minutes
11. The Ruined Water Castle at Djokja – ca. 4 minutes
12. A Court Pageant in Solo – over 3 minutes

ATF122

Preface

"Though we travel the world over to find the beautiful, we must carry it with us, or we find it not."
—Ralph Waldo Emerson

Having traveled extensively in many lands, some near and familiar, others remote and strange, it occurred to me that a musical portrayal of some of the interesting things I had been privileged to see, a tonal description of the impressions and emotions they had awakened, would interest those who are attracted by adventure and picturesqueness and inspired by their poetic reactions.

Who is not at heart a globe-trotter?

Are we not all fascinated by distant countries and strange people?

And so the thought gradually matured in me to recreate my roaming experiences.

This cycle of musical travelogues—tonal journeys—which I have named collectively "Phonoramas," begins with a series of twelve descriptive scenes in Java. I have prefaced each with a brief elucidation.

The Island of Java, called "The Garden of the East," with a population of close to forty million, is the most densely inhabited island in the world. It has a tropical, luxuriant vegetation; marvelous scenery and picturesque inhabitants; huge volcanoes, active and extinct; majestic ruins and imposing monuments of many centuries past.

The Javanese are a docile people, with quaint customs and old traditions. Possessing an ancient culture, they combine originality with proficiency in various arts. It was, however, the native music of the Javanese, in the heart of Java, at Djokja and Solo that made the most profound impression on me.

All Javanese music is in double or quadruple time; triple time does not exist. Its sameness of beat and its monotony of pulsation have a lulling, hypnotizing effect; its polyrhythms, syncopations, triplet-figures and manifold passage-patterns help to stimulate interest. Most of Javanese music is based upon the pentatonic scale.

Of the twelve numbers of this suite, all of which are in duple or quadruple time[1], the first two dances of the *Three Dances*, *In the Kraton* and *A Court Pageant in Solo* are entirely diatonic; *Gamelan, Wayang Purwa, Hari Besaar and Chattering Monkeys*, though mainly diatonic are not consistently so; *Boro Budur, Bromo Volcano*, the third of the *Three Dances*, *The Gardens of Buitenzorg, In the Streets of Old Batavia* and *The Ruined Water Castle at Djokja* are considerably more chromatic.

Although some of the following compositions, or parts thereof, express my impressions in the native music-idiom as *I understood it*, I have neither borrowed nor imitated actual Javanese tunes, designs or harmonies in any of the movements excepting the third; *Hari Besaar*. Here I made use of two fragments of authentic Javanese melodies,

one called Krawita:

the other, Kanjut:

I also used two measures from a Javanese Rhapsody for orchestra, composed by Paul Seelig of Bandong, Java, to whom I take pleasure in expressing my indebtedness for valuable information about Javanese music:

— Leopold Godowsky
New York, May 27, 1925.

[1]My 24 *Walzermasken* and the 30 numbers of my *Triakontameron* are in triple meter exclusively.

Addendum

"Artists, like the Greek gods, are only revealed to one another."

— Oscar Wilde

The thoughtful attention given to the interpretative directions of my compositions has resulted in a profusion of expression marks, pedal indications and fingerings. Though they may appear on the surface as too minute and elaborate, I believe the serious student will find them essential and illuminating. To disregard or alter such indications—in the broader sense—would seem to me as much of a license as a change of any melodic line, harmonic texture, or rhythmic design. Even when all the interpretative signs are scrupulously observed, there yet remains ample scope for self-expression and individuality. To the unthinking this statement may appear paradoxical, but to those who do not seek liberty in lawlessness and originality in individualistic distortions, the truth of this assertion will be apparent.

I deem it necessary to emphasize the importance I attach to the extreme softness of a *pp* mark. To play a genuine *pp*, both concentrated and sustained effort is required.

At the same time I wish to draw attention to the dynamic relativity of all accents, except *sf*, which symbol is of an exclamatory character.

Whenever an accent is provided for each note of a melody, as in the third dance of the *Three Dances*, the purpose is not to accentuate each tone individually, but to give a dynamically *graded* plastic outline to the melodic contour, with proper regard, of course, for proportionate dynamic values in the interrelationship of phrases.

The same principle is applicable to the *tenuto* (–) mark, which demands a clinging to the key, with a barely perceptible dynamic emphasis.

The sign ʌ is a combination of *tenuto* (–) and *sforzando* *sf*, requiring the notes so marked to be both fully sustained and very strongly emphasized.

The task to establish *firmly* an approximately definite rate of speed for any movement, or to indicate undulations of time *within* any movement, presents insurmountable difficulties. Our ever-variable feeling for what would constitute a correct *tempo* and appropriate time-fluctuations for and during a movement, prevents us from deciding definitely and consistently upon a permanently fixed rate of speed. Therefore, I believe that *tempo* designations or metronome marks should be considered as guiding suggestions rather than inflexible directions, although appreciable deviations would lead to misinterpretations. The performer's physical and mental state, his prevailing mood, the *entourage*, the weather, seasonal changes—each and all affect his susceptibility. And the more sensitive and sensitized the artist, the more responsive he is, the more he vibrates and throbs in unison with the known and unknown influences and unfathomable forces, the greater, deeper and finer is his art.

— L.G.
New York, July 11, 1925

1. Gamelan

Native music, played by the Javanese on their indigenous instruments, I called *Gamelan*. The Javanese ensemble is a kind of exotic orchestra, consisting mainly of diversely shaped and constructed percussive instruments of metal, wood and bamboo, comprising various kinds and sizes of bells, chimes, gongs, sounding boards, bowls, pans, drums (some barrel-like), tom-toms, native xylophones, sonorous *alang-alang* (zephyr-like, Aeolian harp-like) and other unique music implements. The only stringed instrument I could discern was the ancient, guitar-shaped *rebab*, which is held by the leader in a position similar to that of the lute.

Both rulers of the two Sultanates of central Java: the Susuhunan of Solo and the Sultan of Djokja, and the two independent princes, Manku Negoro of Solo and Paku Alam of Djokja, have the best largest and most complete native orchestras (*Gamelan*). They own old instruments of inestimable value, the enchanting sonority of which is attributable to the mellowing process of time.

The sonority of the *Gamelan* is so weird, spectral, fantastic and bewitching, the native music so elusive, vague, shimmering and singular, that on listening to this new world of sound I lost my sense of reality, imagining myself in a realm of enchantment. Nothing seen or experienced in Java conveyed so strongly the mysterious and strange character of the island and its inhabitants.

The *Gamelan* produces most ethereal *pianissimos*, particularly entrancing when heard from a distance. It is like a perfume of sound, like a musical breeze. Usually the music, beginning very softly and languidly, becomes faster and louder as the movement progresses, rising, at last, to a barbaric climax.

In this, the first of the descriptive scenes, I have endeavored to recreate a *Gamelan* sonority—a typically Javanese atmosphere. Except for the one chromatic variation (pages 281–82), which is intentionally Occidental, the movement is almost exclusively diatonic and decidedly Oriental (Far Eastern).

1. Gamelan

LEOPOLD GODOWSKY
(1870–1938)

ATF122

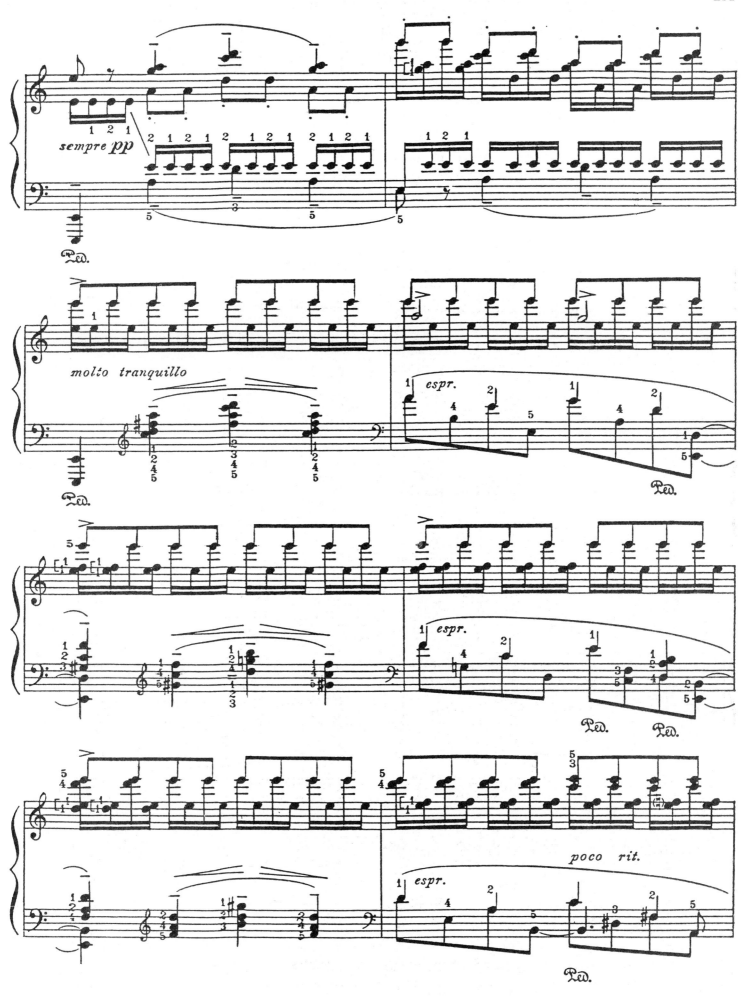

282

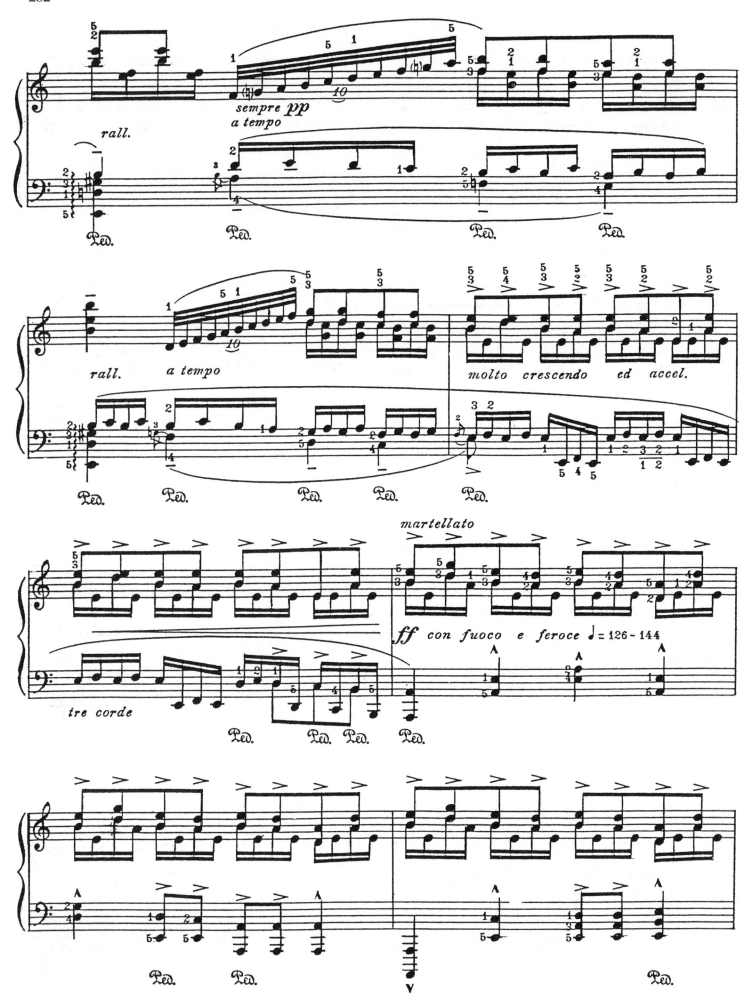

ATF122

sempre *ff* ed agitato

286

ATF122

287

Berlin, Sept. 24th, 1924.

ATF122

2. *Wayang-Purwa*
Puppet Shadow Plays

This ancient, characteristically Javanese quasi-histrionic entertainment, produced on festive occasions, is very popular in Java. It symbolizes to the Javanese their past historical greatness; their hopes, aspirations and national solidarity. To the subdued accompaniment of the *Gamelan*, the *Dalang* — manager, actor, musician, singer, reciter and improviser, all in one — recites classic Hindu epics, or modernized and localized versions of them, or other mythical or historical tales and East Indian legends, while grotesque, flat leather puppets throw shadows on a white screen to interpret and illustrate the reciter's stories. These puppets the *Dalang* manipulates by means of bamboo rods. Wayang-Purwa is somewhat of a combination of Punch and Judy and Chinese shadows.

2. Wayang-Purwa
(Puppet Shadow Plays)

LEOPOLD GODOWSKY

ATF122

New York, November 28th, 1924.

ATF122

3. *Hari Besaar*

The Great Day

The Kermess—the Country Fair—is here.

From plantations and hamlets natives flock to the town that is the center of the bright, joyous celebrations, naive, harmless amusements. They throw themselves eagerly into the whirl of festivities, enjoying the excitement and animation.

Actors, musicians, dancers and fakirs contribute to the pleasures of the people and to the picturesqueness of the scene.

The Great Day — *Hari Besaar!*

3. Hari Besaar
(The Great Day)

LEOPOLD GODOWSKY

304

molto più mosso (stretto)

*) This chord an octave lower, if desired.

New York City, Oct. 27th, 1924.

ATF122

4. Chattering Monkeys at the Sacred Lake of Wendit

The Sacred Lake of Wendit is several miles distant from the attractive little city of Malang. In the woods, near the lake, we find ourselves in one of the numerous Simian colonies of Java, among the aborigines and the forest, enjoying an intimate view of their tribal life. On every side are jabbering monkeys, hundreds of them, jumping from tree to tree, running up and down the trunks and branches, while others, nearer the ground, are springing on and off the roofs of the small hotel and the bath houses, snatching bananas from the visitors.

The scene is full of humor, fun and animation.

4. Chattering Monkeys
at the Sacred Luke of Wendit

LEOPOLD GODOWSKY

310

ATF122

312

New York, Dec. 3rd, 1924.

ATF122

5. *Boro Budur in Moonlight*

On a sacred hill, in the heart of Java, some thirty miles from Djokja, stand the colossal ruins of the most imposing and gigantic Buddhist monument in existence, the world-famous temple of Boro Budur, "The Shrine of the Many Buddhas." No matter how *blasé* the weary traveler may be, he cannot fail to be stirred and bewildered by the stupendous masonry and by the hundreds of sculptured Buddhas, images and bas-reliefs. The amazing dimensions and incredible craftsmanship enrapture the senses; the loftiness of conception, and the luxuriance of imagination thrill the beholder.

In moonlight, Boro Budur is most fantastic. An uncanny, eerie, melancholy mood permeates the whole atmosphere. Deep silence and a sense of strangeness and out-of-the-worldness contribute to the impression of utter desolation and to the feeling of inevitable decay and dissolution of all things earthly, the hopeless struggle of human endeavor against eternity.

ATF122

5. Boro Budur in Moonlight

LEOPOLD GODOWSKY

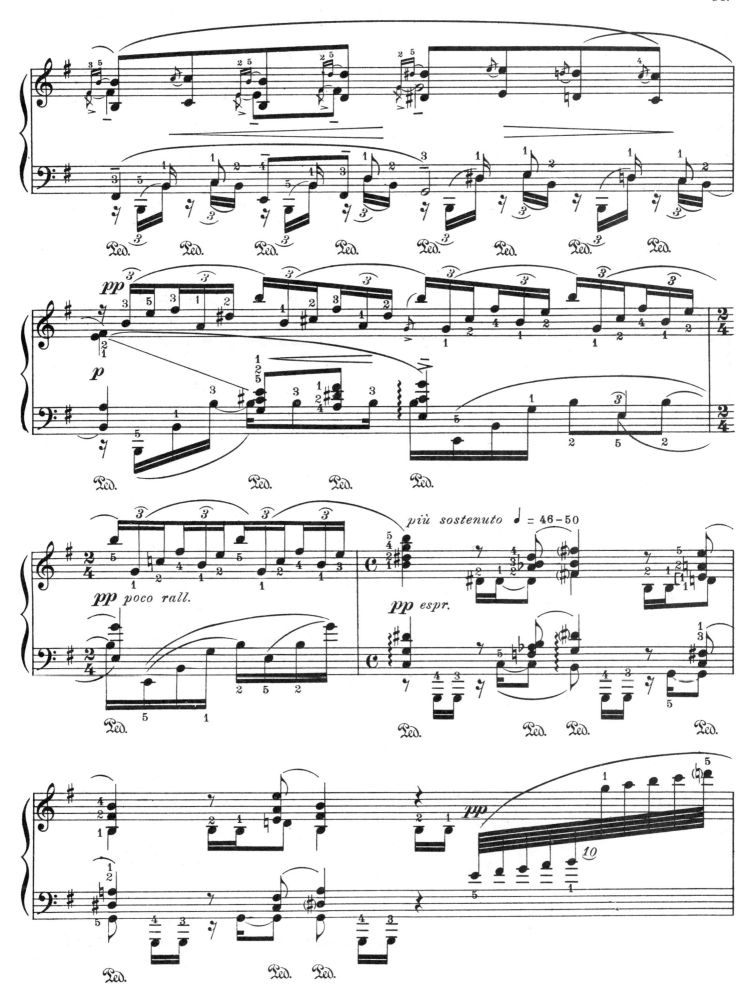

ATF122

320

New York City, November 5th, 1924.

ATF122

6. The Bromo Volcano
and the Sand Sea at Daybreak

Reaching the Sand Sea from Tosari, the most famous mountain resort in Java, we crossed the sea of sand, perhaps the vastest amphitheater in the world, arriving at the Bromo crater at dawn.

A marvelous sunrise enhanced the terrifying hugeness and transcendental grandeur of this awe-inspiring panorama. The boiling, roaring, rumbling subterranean forces, seething and spouting up from abysmal depths, the sulphurous vapors and dense clouds, spreading steadily and menacingly over the horizon, suggested scenes from Dante's *Inferno*, and brought to realization the fact that cataclysmic activities, everlasting fires in the bowels of the earth, threaten all that is alive.

The appalling thought of the frailty of all human institutions was overwhelming. *Cui Bono*?.....

But the bright sun, shedding its glorious light and dispelling all fear and gloom, changed the feeling of a crushing futility into an ecstatic triumphal ode. The mere consciousness that such elemental powers exist alleviates the pain of living. An overpowering feeling of humility, of compassion and tenderness toward all things alive, a passionate adoration for the unknown source of all consciousness, filled the soul.

And then we returned...

6. The Bromo Volcano
and the Sand Sea at Daybreak

LEOPOLD GODOWSKY

ATF122

324

ATF122

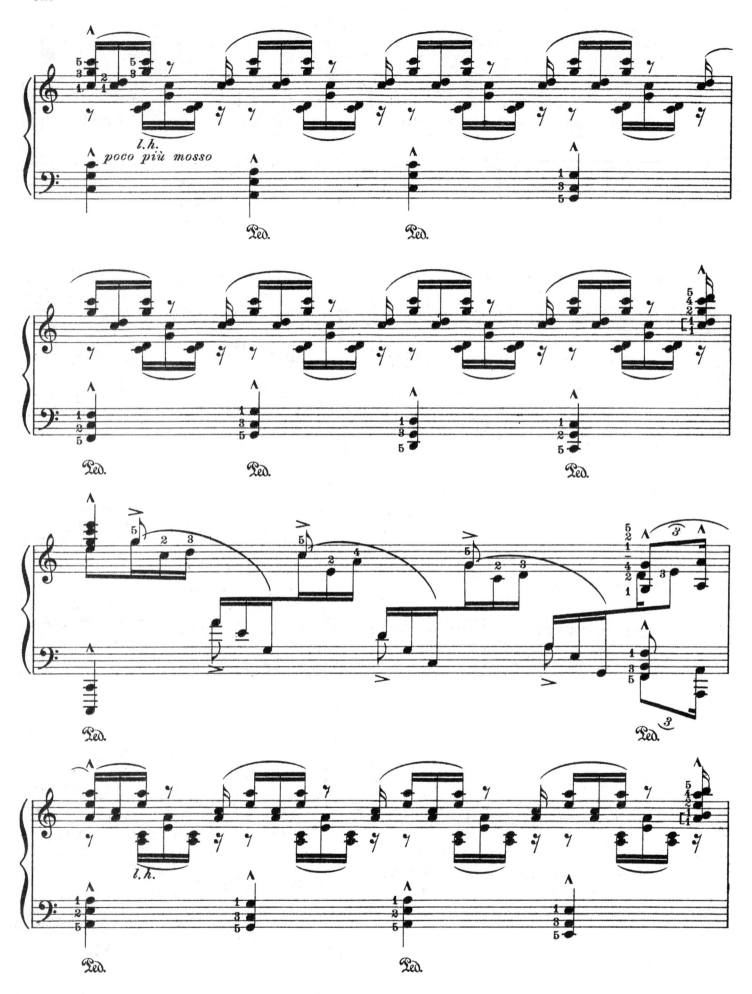

poi a poi a tempo

p subito   sempre cresc.

ATF122

328

ATF122

★) Lower octave, if preferred

New York, Dec. 10th, 1924.

7. Three Dances

It is doubtful if there is a people in any part of the world whose innermost feelings are so wholly revealed in their dances as are the Javanese.

And whether religious or secular, warlike or peaceful, spiritual or sensuous, these dances are always beautiful.

The first of the *Three Dances* expresses the languor and melancholy of the Far East; the second, the grace and charm of the Oriental dancers; the third, their poetry and tenderness, translated into an Occidental idiom.

7. Three Dances

LEOPOLD GODOWSKY

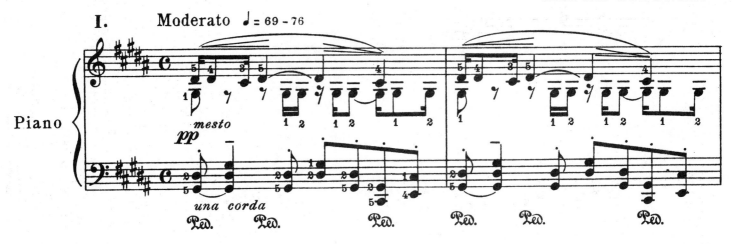

Copyright © 1925 by Carl Fischer, Inc.

ATF122

338

ATF122

344

ATF122

New York, April 4th, 1925.

8. The Gardens of Buitenzorg

Buitenzorg, meaning "Sans Souci" and pronounced Boy-ten-sorg, forty miles from Batavia, is the country capital of Java, where the Governor-General of the Dutch East Indies has his residence. His spacious palace is situated in a large park, which forms part of the most famous Botanical Gardens in the world.

The finest collection of tropical trees, plants and flowers is to be found in the gardens of this distant corner of our Earth. The profusion, richness, magnificence and beauty of this strange horticultural world are unparalleled.

The fragrant frangipanis, the white tuberoses (the Malay call them "The Charmers of the Night") and a bewildering number of other most delicately scented flowers intoxicate the senses.

The heavily perfumed air awakens an inexpressibly deep and painful yearning for unknown worlds, for inaccessible ideals, for past happenings irrevocably gone—these memories which the ocean of time gradually submerges and finally buries in oblivion...

Why do certain scents produce unutterable regrets, insatiable longings, indefinable desires?

8. The Gardens of Buitenzorg

LEOPOLD GODOWSKY

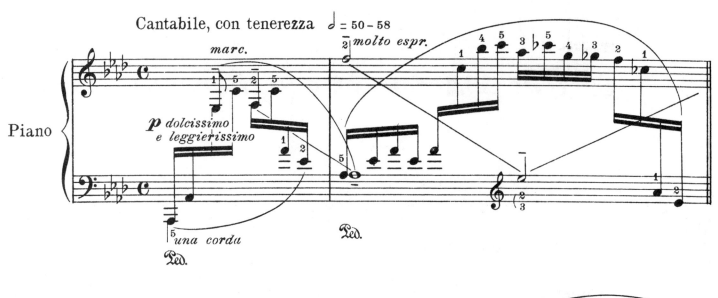

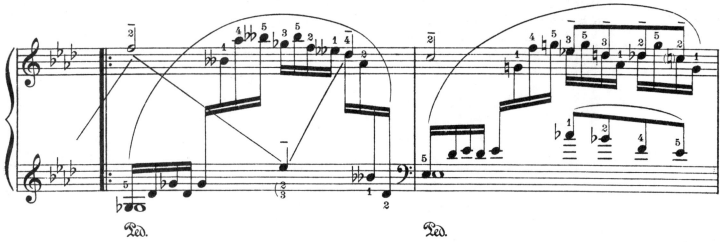

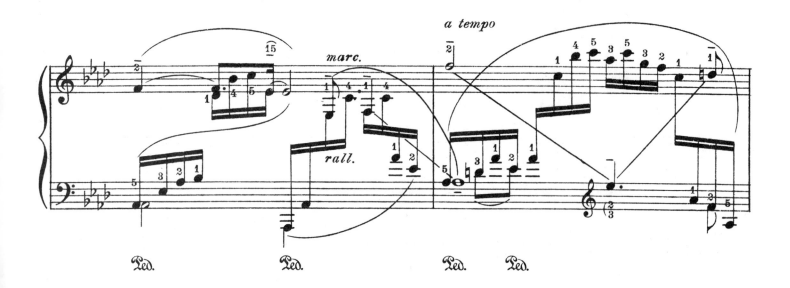

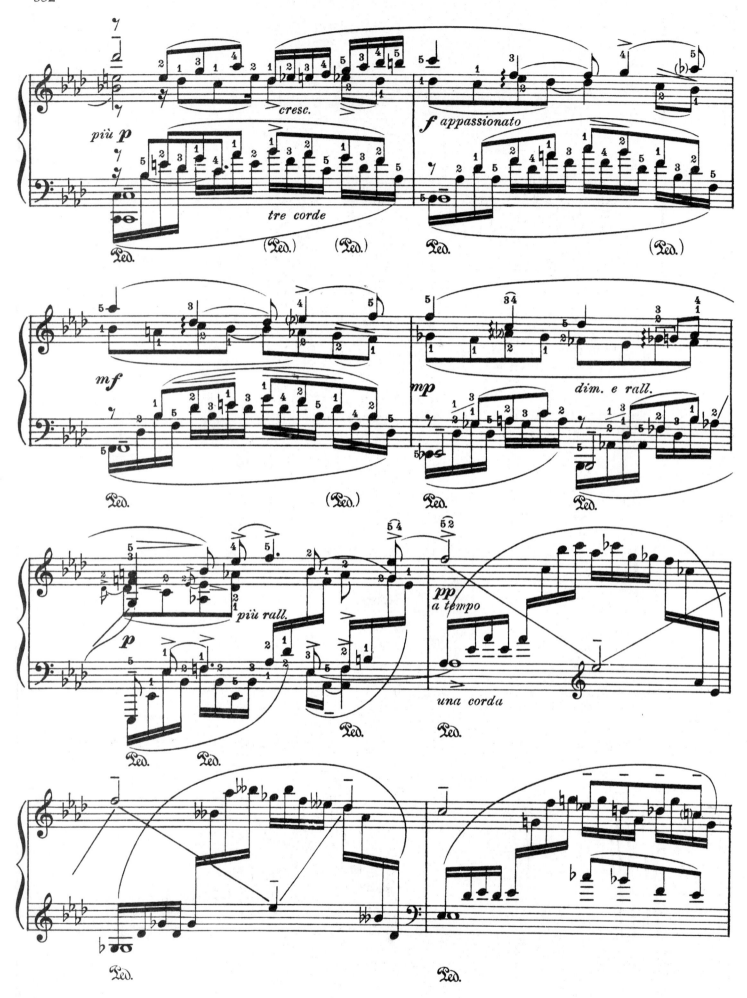

354

Chicago, March 3rd, 1925.

9. *In the Streets of Old Batavia*

To stroll in the old streets of lower Batavia is an exhilarating experience. As we wander near the seashore, through the crowded bazaars and busy, narrow streets, many of which are intersected by bricked canals lined with weather-beaten buildings in the Dutch style, we meet exotic crowds, consisting mainly of Chinese, Arabs, natives and other Asians, interspersed with Europeans, of whom the Dutch form a large majority.

A ramble through the hectic Chinese quarter leads us to a quiet and contemplative corner of the Arab settlement. Another turn brings us to the native quarter. And when the bazaars are reached, a kaleidoscopic, multifarious conglomeration of humans bewilders even the most seasoned globe-trotter.

9. In the Streets of Old Batavia

Presto, con brio *about* ♩ = 69 - 76

LEOPOLD GODOWSKY

Piano

f articolato

360

ATF122

366

*) The pedal may be held till the end.

Evanston, Ill. May 21st, 1925.

10. In the Kraton

Surakarta, popularly called Solo, and Djokjakarta, commonly shortened to Djokja, are the most important and interesting native cities in Java.

The greatest ruler – the Susuhunan – resides in Solo, while the next in importance, the Sultan of Djokja, lives in the last named capital. In the heart of each capital is a vast enclosure called the *Kraton*, in which the potentate has his palaces and wherein dwell besides the Sultan, Sultana and princes and princesses, his numerous concubines, slaves and servants, court officials, nobles, musicians, actors, dancers, workmen, tradespeople and many individuals with indefinable occupations. Each *Kraton* has a population of between ten and fifteen thousand, the ensemble constituting a court of huge dimensions.

It is evening. Quaint scenes charm our vision. Faint sounds of the entrancing *Gamelan* fill the fragrant air. The seemingly unreal reality casts a hypnotic spell over our consciousness.

There is poetry in every ebbing moment.

It is evening in the Orient...

10. In the Kraton

LEOPOLD GODOWSKY

ATF122

372

ATF122

378

ATF122

ATF122

poco più mosso e sempre ***pp***

poco a poco più mosso

Ped.　　　Ped.　　　Ped.　　　Ped.

Chicago, Feb. 18th, 1925.

ATF122

11. The Ruined Water Castle at Djokja

Near the *Kraton* of Djokja, deserted, fallen into decay, stand the moldy and crumbling remains of the once resplendent Water Palace, with its murmuring fountains and splashing cascades, with its aquatic pranks and air-filling scents of exotic flowers.

Where once was merriment, there is now the mystery and romance of vanished days, the sadness of evanescent pleasures.

The fountains and cascades murmur memories of yesteryears—yearning for past joys, mourning for departed love....

11. The Ruined Water Castle at Djokja

LEOPOLD GODOWSKY

Allegretto mormorando ed armonioso (♩ = 104 – 116)

390

ATF122

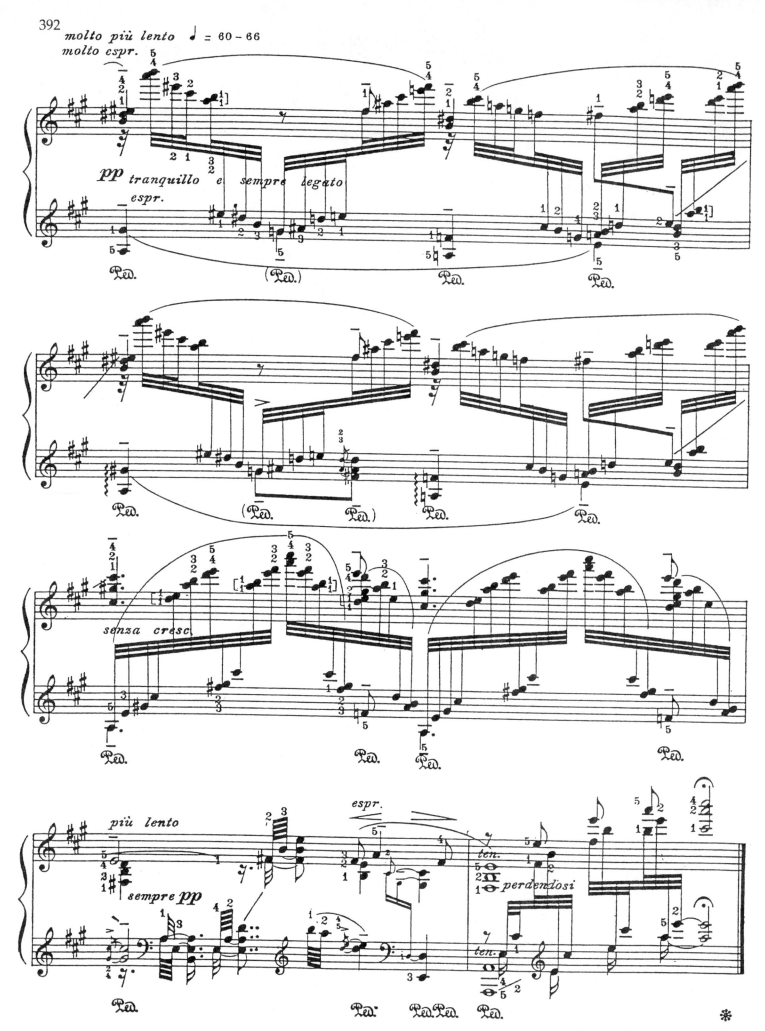

Chicago, January 25th, 1925.

12. A Court Pageant in Solo

The pomp, bombast and gorgeousness of a royal procession on a festive occasion or court function in either of the two native capitals make a dazzling and grotesque spectacle. The exuberance and abandon of the natives, the force and charm of the native rhythms, challenge description.

The clanging and clashing march opens the event. Strongly emphasized in the middle section (F# minor) of this closing composition is that strain of sadness ever present in the music of the Orient. The hilarious mood is resumed with the *Fugato*, which leads back to an intensified version of the barbaric march.

And here these tonal journeys come to an end.

12. A Court Pageant in Solo

LEOPOLD GODOWSKY

ATF122

Tempo primo ♩ = 96–108

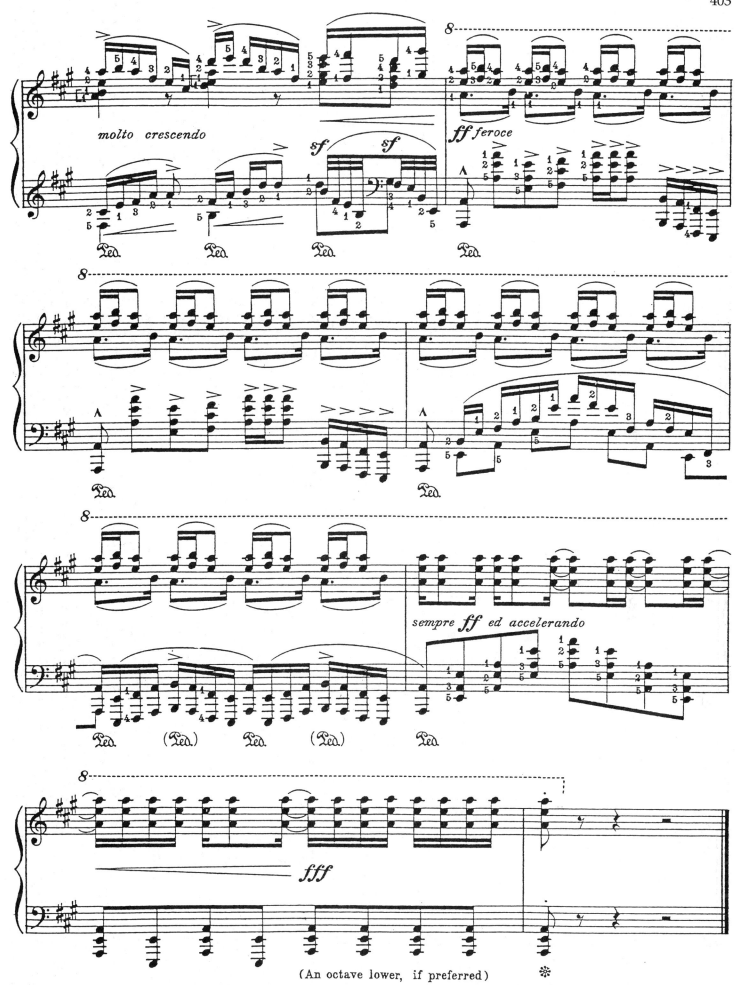

(An octave lower, if preferred)

Chicago, February 24th, 1925.

Passacaglia

for piano solo

Prefatory Remarks

The theme of my Passacaglia is based upon the first 8 measures of Schubert's Unfinished Symphony. This Passacaglia consists of 44 variations, a cadenza and a fugue. The analysis and description of and comment upon this work I leave to the serious student and interested scholar.

This composition, written on the eve of the one hundredth anniversary of Franz Schubert's death, is my heartfelt tribute to this precious and prolific genius, who, despite his short and uneventful life, succeeded so admirably in translating our innermost emotions into music.

With the exception of Chopin, I know of no other composer whose lyricisms have touched the heart of so many; whose melodies have become so thoroughly the treasured property of all civilized nations; whose tone-imageries have so sensitized and refined our poetic susceptibilities.

I will feel fully rewarded, should this contribution to the approaching commemoration prove to be worthy of the occasion.

— Leopold Godowsky
Atlantic City, New Jersey

November 7, 1927

Passacaglia

LEOPOLD GODOWSKY
(1870–1938)

*) The theme of the Passacaglia snould stand out in all variations, sufficiently to be noticed, but not too prominently when it is not the leading voice.

408

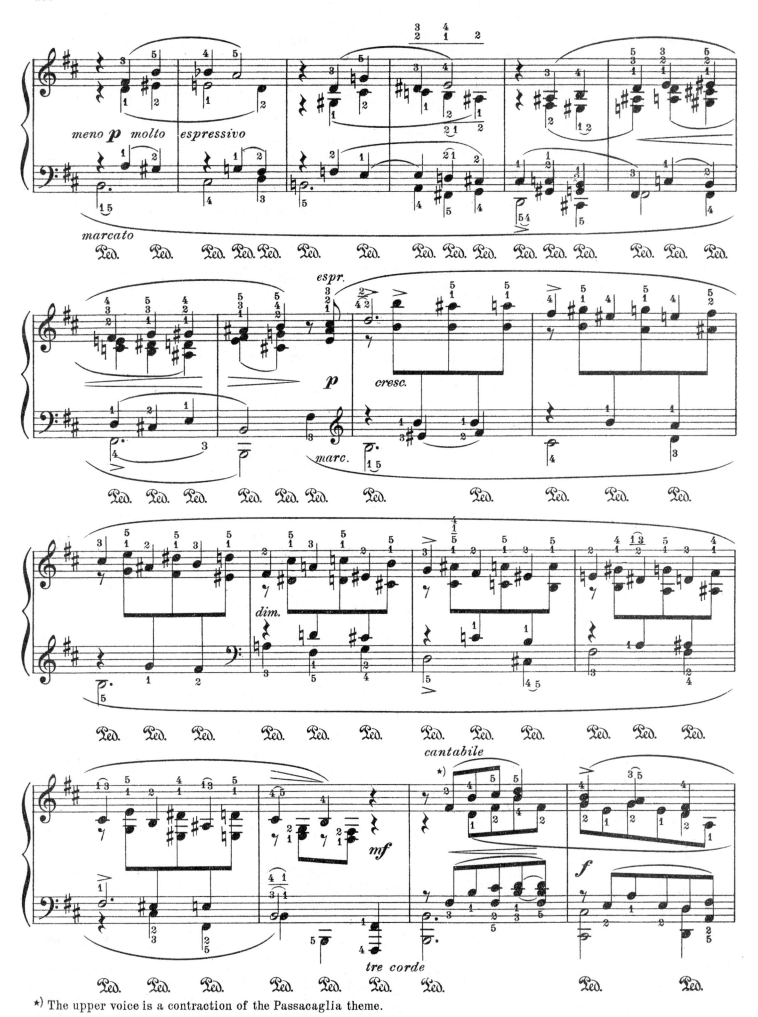

*) The upper voice is a contraction of the Passacaglia theme.

413

ATF122

senza pedale

sempre pp

Ped.   Ped.   Ped.

Ped.   Ped.   Ped.   Ped.   Ped.   (Ped.)   Ped.   Ped.   Ped.

molto cresc. ed agitato

sf

ff con fuoco

tre corde

Ped.   (Ped.)   Ped.   Ped.   (Ped.)   Ped.   Ped.   (Ped.)   Ped.

Allegro moderato
non legato, articolato

marc.

con brio

più f

non legato

418

★) This ♮C may be played by the fifth finger of the left hand.

ATF122

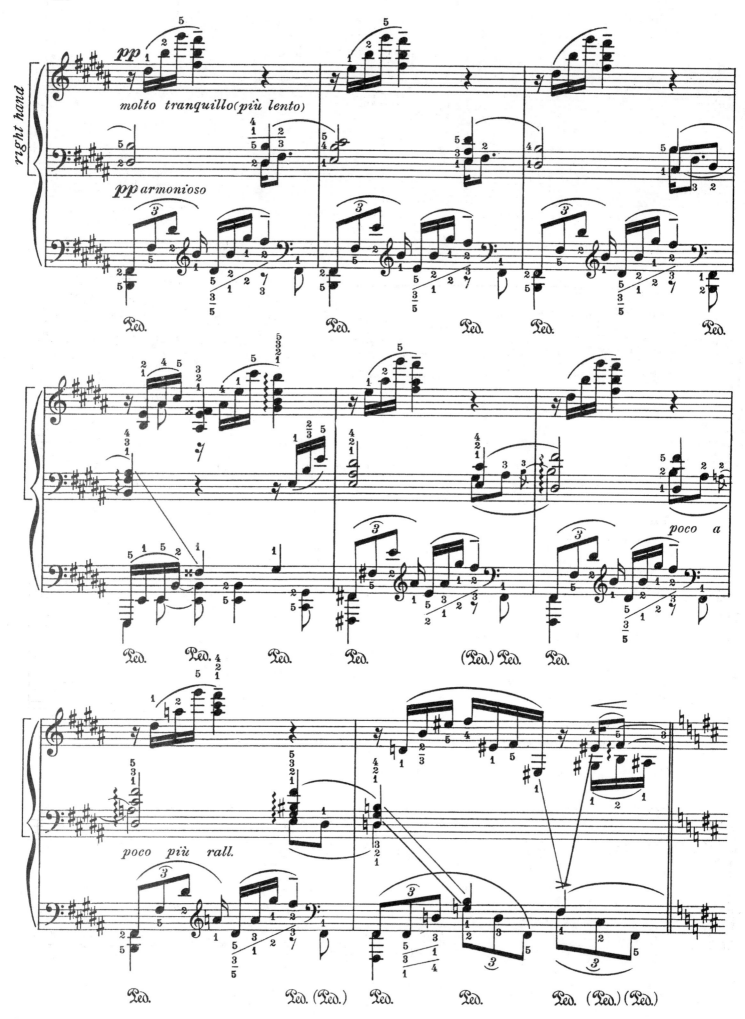

con brio sempre **ff** e non legato

Allegretto grazioso

★) A faster trill is advisable.

436

*) If the omission of the Fugue is desired, the Passacaglia should end here.

Atlantic City, N.J., September 25th, 1927.

ATF122

Andante espressivo *(Epilogue)*

Fuga

Andante sostenuto (about ♩.=46)

una 3 corda

440

*) The accents should be played softly and expressively; the theme should stand out unobtrusively.

★) The accented notes should be played very softly and expressively; the theme should stand out unobtrusively.

maestoso

(Inversion of the Theme)

(Augmentation of the Theme)

leggiero

f *p* subito

un poco più mosso

f *p* subito

left hand

⋆) The stems upward are intended for the right hand, downward, for the left hand.

*) In the following eleven measures, the Organ-point must be emphasized persistently.

447

New York, October 21st, 1927.

ATF122

To my dear old friend Alexander Lambert, from his devoted Leopold Godowsky New York July 1916.

ATF122